Participant Book
Catechumenate
Year C

Foundations in Faith

Bob Duggan • Carol Gura

Rita Ferrone • Gael Gensler

Steve Lanza • Donna Steffen

Maureen A. Kelly

RCL

Allen, Texas

Contents

Nihil Obstat
Reverend George Smiga, S.T.D.
Censor Librorum

Imprimatur
† *Most Reverend Anthony Pilla*
Bishop of Cleveland

May, 2000

The Nihil Obstat and Imprimatur are official declarations that the material reviewed is free of doctrinal or moral error. No implication is contained therein that those granting the Nihil Obstat and Imprimatur agree with the contents, opinions, or statements expressed.

Acknowledgments
Scripture excerpts are taken from the *New Revised Standard Version* Bible Copyright © 1993, 1989, by the Division of Christian Education of the National Council of the Churches of Christ in the U.S.A. Used by permission.

Send all inquiries to:
RCL • Resources for Christian Living
200 East Bethany Drive
Allen, Texas 75002-3804

Toll free 877-275-4725
Fax   800-688-8356

Printed in the United States of America

12713 ISBN 0-7829-0767-9

6 7 8 9 10 11 12
07 08 09 10 11 12

ADVENT
SEASON

First Sunday of Advent

Scripture:

Jeremiah 33:14-16
Psalm 25:4-5, 8-9, 10, 14
1 Thessalonians 3:12–4:2
Luke 21:25-28, 34-36

Focus:

THE SECOND COMING OF CHRIST

Reflection

Directions: *Think of a time in your own life when you had to wait patiently and be alert for something. (Waiting for the birth of a baby. Anticipating the start of a new job. Waiting news in the doctor's office on serious tests taken. Preparing to move from one city to another.) In the space below write your story of waiting. Describe the circumstances, your feelings and any encouragement you received from your relationship with God and others.*

Questions

1. *How have you gained some measure of calm and security in the midst of your own "advents?"*

2. *When have you waited for the Lord to act in your life? What was the outcome?*

Quotable Quotes

The contemporary American Catholic writer, Walker Percy, known for his novels about the end of the world, says of his work, "A serious novel about the destruction of the United States and the end of the world should perform the function of prophecy in reverse. The novelist writes about the coming end in order to warn about present ills and so avert the end. [H]e is like the canary that coal miners used to take down into the shaft to test the air. When the canary gets unhappy, utters plaintive cries, and collapses, it may be time for the miners to surface and think things over."
[Notes for a "Novel About the End of the World," from *The Message in the Bottle* (New York: Farrar, Straus and Giroux, 1979)]

Did You Know?

The feast of St. Nicholas is celebrated on December 6. Nicholas, patron of sailors and children, was a bishop of the 4th century from whom the Santa Claus tradition developed. Legends and stories of his miracles led to the practice of gift giving in his name at Christmas and to the change of his name, St. Nicholas, into Sint Klaes by the Dutch and then to Santa Claus.

The Church Says:

The Second Vatican Council taught that far from promoting passivity, the expectation of "a new heavens" and a "new earth" should energize us. In the document on the church, the bishops of the world stated, "The expectancy of a new earth should spur us on, for it is here that the body of a new human family grows, foreshadowing in some way the age which is yet to come. . . .When we have spread on earth the fruits of our nature and our enterprise . . . according to the command of the Lord and in his Spirit, we will find them once again, cleansed this time from the stain of sin, illuminated and transfigured, when Christ presents to his Father an eternal and universal kingdom. . ."

The *Catechism of the Catholic Church* examines the doctrine of Christ's return in several places. In its treatment of the Profession of Faith, the catechism stresses several key points. Catholics do not believe that fulfillment of the destiny of creation and human beings will be brought about by material progress or human activity alone (secularism), but by God. Catholics reject any attempts to predict the end of the world (millenarianism) or to lessen in any way our responsibility for stewardship of this present world based on a future second coming of Christ. Catholics believe that we meet the glorified Lord upon the event of our death, as well as when his full glory is revealed to all the world at the end of time.

For This Week:

I want to remember:

I want to put my faith into action by:

Questions to Explore

Prayer for the Week

O Promised One of God,
come and dwell with us
amidst the rush for gifts,
long lines of waiting
lists of things to do.
Let not this season be our undoing,
but a persistent peace,
a content confidence,
and a gentle time of giving;
That your expected arrival into the upheaval
of our lives may bring us
to birth you again and again.
Amen.

Scripture:

Baruch 5:1-9
Psalm 126:1-2, 2-3, 4-5, 6
Philippians 1:4-6, 8-11
Luke 3:1-6

Focus:

HOPE FOR SALVATION

Reflection On My Spiritual Journey

Directions: *Draw a road or path in the space below. This path is winding, rough, and has peaks and valleys. This path represents your life journey. Indicate the peaks (times when God felt close at hand) and valleys (times you felt separated from God) the rough ways (times of struggle or crises) and winding ways (times you were spiritually off course).*

Questions

1. *How has God's presence made your path smooth and straight as you follow the Lord?*

2. *What vision of God's salvation keeps you on this journey?*

3. *Where do you find hope for your journey in these scriptures?*

Did You Know?

Artists frequently portray John the Baptist pointing, for his prophetic role is to point the way to Jesus. Medieval cathedrals were deliberately designed to show the place of the prophets in the economy of salvation. The prophets, whose challenging words were associated with the chill north wind, were depicted on the north wall, while the wall to the south, associated with warmer and gentler climes, was reserved for depictions of the saints. In the new world, John the Baptist is revered as the patron saint of Puerto Rico.

The Church Says:

This Sunday the promise of salvation, and therefore our hope, is given direction by the figure of John the Baptist. In the preface for Masses of John the Baptist, the Church addresses God, praying, "You chose John the Baptist from all the prophets to show the world its redeemer, the lamb of sacrifice." (*Roman Missal*, Preface 61). John the Baptist directs us to the object of our longing. He points the way to our hope.

In this vein, St. Augustine preached: God established a time for his promises and a time for their fulfillment. The time for promises was in the prophets, until John the Baptist . . . God, who is faithful, put himself in our debt, not by receiving anything but by promising so much. A promise was not sufficient for him; he chose to commit himself in writing as well . . . . He has promised [us] divinity, mortals immortality, sinners justification, the poor a rising to glory. . . . [B]ecause God's promises seemed impossible. . .God. . .established a mediator of his good faith, not a prince or angel or archangel, but his only Son. All this had therefore to be prophesied, foretold, and impressed on us as an event in the future, in order that we might wait for it in faith, not find it a sudden and dreadful reality. (In Psalm 109, 1-3: CCL 40, 1601-1603 and quoted in Liturgy of the Hours, Office of Readings, Wednesday, Second Week of Advent.)

For This Week:

I want to remember:

I want to put my faith into action by:

Questions to Explore

Prayer for the Week

Awaken my heart, O God,
that I might watch and wait
for the signs of Christ's coming.
Stir in me advent's assurance that this birth
will not go unnoticed,
will not be in vain,
will not be dampened.
Shake me free from my winding ways,
fill my valleys with hope,
level my peaks with serenity
As I prepare a place for the Incarnated One.

Scripture:

Zephaniah 3:14-18a
Isaiah 12: 2-3, 4, 5-6
Philippians 4:4-7
Luke 3:10-18

Focus:

MORAL CONVERSION

Reflection On My Spiritual Journey

Directions: *Below is a list of the cardinal virtues with a descriptive definition. Think about each virtue in your life, both in terms of attitude and actions. Under each virtue, write a sentence describing to what degree that virtue has taken root in your life. Be sure to mention a specific example of the lack of or the practice of the virtue.*

Cardinal virtues direct the individual to lead a humanly good life.

Prudence *is practical wisdom that enables the individual to discern specific actions that will best fulfill the requirements of authentic virtuous living in particular situations.*

Justice *disposes one to practice fairness in dealing with others.*

Fortitude *empowers one to aim for the good in the face of contrary fears and opposition.*

Temperance *helps the individual maintain a correct balance and appropriate limits in pursuing sensual pleasures.*

Questions

1. *How has God's presence made your path smooth and straight as you follow the Lord?*

2. *What vision of God's salvation keeps you on this journey?*

3. *Where do you find hope for your journey in these scriptures?*

Did You Know?

The third Sunday of Advent is known traditionally as "Gaudete Sunday." *Gaudete* is a Latin word meaning rejoice—an imperative taken from the readings of this day, especially the Pauline readings in all three years of the lectionary cycle. The vigorously practical preaching of the fierce man of the desert, John, assures that we may not take this command to rejoice as a call for superficial cheeriness or an escape from necessary hard choices. On the other hand, the first and second readings, as well as the psalm, forbid us to imagine that the moral life is a set of grim duties. The call to moral conversion is an invitation to lasting joy.

The Church Says:

Catholic teaching upholds that moral conversion is possible for all and needed by all. The final document issued by the Second Vatican Council, "Gaudium et Spes," exhorts the world, "Let everyone consider it . . .[a] sacred duty to count social obligations among [one's] chief duties today and observe them as such. . . . This will be realized only if individuals and groups practice moral and social virtues and foster them in social living. Then. . .there will arise a new generation. . . the molders of a new humanity." (GS 30)

Thus the Council called for moral conversion. This conversion is accomplished in many ways through daily living. Gestures of reconciliation, concern for the poor, the exercise and defense of justice, the admission of one's faults, fraternal correction, and acceptance of suffering are outward signs of this moral conversion. In other words, moral conversion takes time and practice but is accessible to all. The difference between an average piano player and a superb one is the virtuosity that comes with long practice fueled by innate skill and the desire to be truly good. Similarly, moral virtues are fueled by the innate sensibility instilled in us by God and are the result of practicing goodness over time.

For This Week:

I want to remember:

I want to put my faith into action by:

Questions to Explore

Prayer for the Week

December 17
O Wisdom, O holy Word of God,
  you govern all creation
    with your strong yet tender care,
Come and show your people
  the way to salvation.

December 18
O sacred Lord of ancient Israel,
who showed yourself to Moses
  in the burning bush,
who gave him the holy law
  on Sinai mountain:
come, stretch out your mighty hand
  to set us free.

December 19
O Flower of Jesse's stem,
  you have been raised up
  as a sign for all peoples;

kings stand silent in your presence;
the nations bow down in worship
  before you.
Come, let nothing keep you from
  coming to our aid.

December 20
O Key of David, O royal Power of
  Israel
controlling at your will
  the gate of heaven:
Come, break down the prison walls
  of death
for those who dwell in darkness
  and the shadow of death;
and lead your captive people into
  freedom.

Fourth Sunday of Advent

Scripture:

Micah 5:1-4a
Psalm 80:2-3, 15-16, 18-19
Hebrews 10:5-10
Luke 1:39-45

Focus:

THE WORD MADE FLESH

Reflection

Directions: Create a mind map in the space below. A mind map is a way of graphically picturing a flow of consciousness derived from reflecting on words and images. For this map, write the words, 'Jesus—the Word Made Flesh,' in the center. Branching out from that image of Christ, draw lines and write your insights on them. The lines you draw may branch out into several additional lines of insights and images. This is a creative way of drawing out all of the implications of Jesus' humanity for you.

Questions

1. *How would you summarize the significance of Jesus birth?*

2. *How can you more consciously bear Christ in the world today?*

3. *How does the human birth of Jesus speak to the sacredness of life in all its forms?*

Quotable Quotes

"Human life finds itself most vulnerable when it enters the world
and when it leaves the realm of time
to embark upon eternity."

John Paul II, Evangelium Vitae #44.1

Did You Know?

The much-loved story of the Visitation is frequently depicted in church art. One particularly famous example is found in the sculptures on the central portal of Reims Cathedral in France. The beautifully molded figures of Mary and Elizabeth, draped in garments reminiscent of ancient Greece and Rome, are considered by art historians to represent the high point of Gothic classicism.

The Church Says:

As Advent draws to a close, the readings call our attention to the mystery of Christ's coming in the flesh. The reading from the prophet Micah compares the people of Israel waiting for divine deliverance to a woman in labor, giving birth to a child. The letter to the Hebrews takes special account of the importance of the body of Jesus. His body is accepted by the pre-existent savior as "prepared for me" by God's will. His body is obediently offered in sacrifice, surpassing all the sacrifices of the old covenant. Last of all, today's passage from Luke's gospel turns on the mystery of life taking shape in the womb of Mary.

Jesus the Christ is both human and divine. The humanity of Jesus is key to understanding his divinity. In the person of Jesus, God and humankind come together in perfect unity. You, like Mary and Elizabeth, are also blessed because you have heard and believed. A soul that believes both conceives and brings forth the Word of God and acknowledges his works.

For This Week:

I want to remember:

I want to put my faith into action by:

Questions to Explore

Prayer for the Week

December 21
O Radiant Dawn,
*   splendor of eternal light,*
*   sun of justice:*
come, shine on those who dwell in darkness
*   and the shadow of death.*

December 22
O King of all the nations,
*   the only joy of every human heart;*
O Keystone of the mighty arch of man,
come and save the creature you
*   fashioned from the dust.*

December 23
O Emmanuel, king and lawgiver,
*   desire of the nations,*
Savior of all people,
*   come and set us free, Lord our God.*

CHRISTMAS SEASON

Christmas, Mass During the Day

Scripture:

Isaiah 52:7-10
Psalm 98:1, 2-3, 3-4, 5-6
Hebrews 1:1–6
John 1:1-18 [or 1:1-5, 9-14]

Focus:

CHRIST CAME FOR OUR SALVATION.

Reflection

Directions: *Think about Jesus' presence in your life over the past several months: Times when you were confused and troubled; times of great happiness and peace; times when you longed to know Jesus more deeply. Write about your experience using the format of a table of contents for a book. Begin by naming the chapters of your experience of the Lord. Include a one-sentence description of the contents of that chapter. When you have finished the chapters, name the book.*

Title

Chapter I

Chapter II

Chapter III

Chapter IV

Chapter V

Questions

1. *What did this exercise teach you about the presence of Jesus in your life?*

2. *How will you continue to live Christmas all through the year?*

Memorable People

On the day after Christmas, December 26, the feast of the first martyr is celebrated, **St. Stephen**. The following day, December 27, the Church celebrates the feast of **St. John**, apostle and evangelist.

Did You Know?

In the thirteenth century, St. Francis of Assisi popularized the use of figurines to depict the Christmas message. But as early as the fourth century, representations of the nativity of the Lord were painted as wall decorations depicting not only the infancy narrative accounts of Christ's birth, but also the words of the prophets Isaiah and Habakkuk, that the Messiah would be born in the midst of animals in a manger. (See *Book of Blessings*, 1541, for more background information and the blessing prayers over the manger scene.)

The Church Says:

This feast celebrates the Incarnation. The eternal Word of God became flesh in Jesus. God's love is not distant but draws near to us, giving us the opportunity to become children of God. St. Augustine meditates: "For what greater grace could God have made to dawn on us than to make his only Son become the son of man, so that a son of man might in turn become son of God? . . .Ask if this were merited; ask for its reason, for its justification, and see whether you will find any other answer but sheer grace." (Sermon 185: PL 38, 997-99.)

We did not merit the Incarnation by our own actions. This gift is given through the initiative of God. The Church proclaims: "In the wonder of the incarnation your eternal Word has brought to the eyes of faith a new and radiant vision of your glory. In him we see our God made visible and so are caught up in the love of the God we cannot see" (Preface for Christmas I).

For This Week:

I want to remember:

I want to put my faith into action by:

Questions to Explore

Prayer for the Week

Your glory came to dwell among us
as Word became flesh.
You, who shower the night sky with stars
announce his coming into my life.
Give me the eyes of a child
that I might see this holy child of light.
Give me a heart flowing like the rivers of stars
that I might spread the news
of this wondrous birth;
in all the ways I love
and give
and rejoice.
Be born in me that I might live anew.

Scripture:

1 Samuel 1:20-22, 24-28
Psalm 84:2-3, 5-6, 9-10
1 John 3:1-2, 21-24
Luke 2:41-52

Focus:

THE FAMILY IS THE DOMESTIC CHURCH.

Reflection On My Spiritual Journey

Directions: *Take some time to re-create your family tree. List ancestors you remember or you know of, and include those who follow you. You are in the center of this family tree. When you have completed naming the members of your family, jot down some characteristics and values held by the specific members. Look for common threads through the generations. Draw lines to indicate the major connections between members.*

Questions

1. *What examples of holiness have come from your family members?*

2. *How have the relationships in your family influenced your life, values, and spirituality?*

Did You Know?

The Feast of the Holy Family is a modern addition to the universal calendar of the Roman Church since 1921, when it was placed as the First Sunday after Epiphany. Like many feasts added in modern times, its emphasis tends to be more on a doctrinal theme than some specific action of God. Its contemporary character is also shown by the way that it seeks to instruct and inspire through an obvious appeal to sentiment and emotion.

The placement of Holy Family Sunday in the Christmas season is an even more recent adjustment to the calendar, stemming from the reform of 1969. Situated so closely to Christmas, today's celebration cannot help but resonate with overtones of the Incarnation. By highlighting the family as the context into which Jesus was born, today's liturgy reinforces the fact of his full humanity.

The Church Says:

In the decree on the laity from the Second Vatican Council, the Church also contemplates the role of the family. The world bishops stated, "The mission of being the primary vital cell of society has been given to the family by God. This mission will be accomplished if the family, by the mutual affection of its members and by family prayer, presents itself as a domestic sanctuary of the church; if the whole family takes its part in the church's liturgical worship; if, finally, it offers active hospitality and practices justice and other good works for the benefit of all its sisters and brothers who suffer from want." (AA II)

The *Catechism* continues this theme of the role of the family in society, teaching that the Christian family is a communion of persons whose love and unity resemble that of the Holy Trinity. Furthermore, the family is called to participate in Christ's prayer and self-offering to the Father, and to grow in charity through daily prayer and reading of Sacred Scripture. The Christian family is charged in its daily life with the work of evangelization, and furthering the mission of the Church. Thus it is the vocation of Christian parents to initiate their children into society through family life and the communion of love, moral values, faith and worship that is nurtured there.

For This Week:

I want to remember:

I want to put my faith into action by:

Questions to Explore

Prayer for the Week

Lord, Giver of Life, we are grateful
    for all those who have come
    before us
        in our families,
    those we have known and
    those ancestors whom
        we have never met or
        heard about.
This lineage of parents,
    grandparents,
    great-grandparents
    and so many others
has gifted us with life, faith and our
    family story.
This story was chosen by You from
    all time.
This tradition of holy parents is
    one of many signs of your
    faithful love.

May the threads of this story and
    the strands of tradition
        which encircle our families,
        be cherished for generations
        to come.
May we express our gratitude to You
    and to our ancestors
        by passing on these rich
        traditions,
        this holiness
        and this story,
    to the next generation.
We bless and praise you,
    Heavenly Parent,
    You have been so generous
    with us.
Amen.

Epiphany

Scripture:

Isaiah 60:1-6
Psalm 72:1-2, 7-8, 10-11, 12-13
Ephesians 3:2-3a, 5-6
Matthew 2:1-12

Focus:

CHRIST IS THE LIGHT OF ALL NATIONS.

Reflection

Directions: *Slowly read this story of light. Then answer the questions below.*

In the time of long before tomorrow, Nicholas, a potter, and his wife, Christina, lived and loved in a tiny little village. They never had children of their own, but their love for each other and their neighbors was very widely known. Nicolas would work in his downstairs pottery shop and people would drop in to share their dreams and failures. Christina would always have time to listen to the stories of friends and strangers as she wove the daily household chores with their dreams and troubles. In short, the villagers became their children.

Nicholas never questioned the practice of his father and grandfather who were also potters. Each day he would follow their routine of taking two new pots out into the daylight, collecting the light and sealing one of the jars and putting it on the shelf. He would place the other jar of that day's light in his window to light the night. He never knew why he was trained to collect the light and store the sealed pot of light on the shelves that lined his shop. There were rows and rows of sealed jars of light surrounding his workroom.

When a neighbor with a particularly sad story came to Nicholas one day, he and Christina were deeply moved by the darkness that filled the neighbor's heart. Without thinking, Nicholas reached for one of the jars of light and gave it to the man saying, "A gift, a gift of light for you, if you should ever need a place away from darkness." The neighbor never opened the jar, simply knowing the light there was enough to fill the darkness of this troubled man.

From that day on, whenever anyone in darkness came to Nicholas or Christina, they listened to the story, healing it with understanding and compassion. Then they would offer the person a sealed jar of light. None who came in illness, pain or sadness ever needed to open the jar. Just the knowledge that the light was there was enough. (Adapted from: Joseph J Juknialis, "Sealed With a Dream" in Winter Dreams And Other Such Friendly Dragons, (Saratoga CA: Resource Publications, 1979, pp. 11-15).

Questions

1. *Describe your experience of Christ's light, illuminating your times of darkness.*

2. *How can you offer others the light of Christ in your daily encounters?*

Quotable Quotes

"Today you revealed in Christ your eternal plan of salvation and showed him as the light of all peoples."
(Preface for Epiphany, *Roman Missal*)

Did You Know?

The "twelve days of Christmas" are counted from December 25 to January 6, the day of Epiphany. In some cultures, children receive gifts on this day, a reminder of the wise men who brought gifts of gold, frankincense and myrrh to Jesus. In Puerto Rico, for example, on the eve of January 6 ("Three Kings Day"), children fill shoes with hay for the camels and horses of the Magi. The next day the hay is gone, replaced with toys and candy. In Italy the "good witch" Befana (a derivation of the word Epiphany) leaves people surprises accompanied by Rudolfo, who threatens punishment to people who need to encouragement to change for the better. Befana originally intended to join the Magi, but lost heart and so must now go in search of the Christ from house to house, seeing in everyone she meets the "light of all nations." (Mary Ellen Hynes, *Companion to the Calendar*, Liturgy Training Publications, 1993, pages 9-10.)

The Church Says:

Reflecting on the mystery of the Church, the Second Vatican Council wrote, "Christ is the light of all nations; and it is, accordingly, the heartfelt desire of this sacred Council. . . .that, by proclaiming his Gospel to every creature (cf. Mark 16:15), it may bring to all. . .that light of Christ which shines out visibly from the Church." (LG 1) The Church's self-understanding described in the dogmatic constitution on the church, *Lumen Gentium*, is embodied in today's feast which proclaims that all people are attracted to and find salvation in the radiance of God's light. In *Lumen Gentium* Number 15-17, the bishops addressed the church's relationship with other Christians (15) and with non-Christians (16), emphasizing that the church's mandate from the Lord himself is ultimately to preach God's offer of salvation to the very ends of the earth (17). Epiphany means "showing forth" or "manifestation." In the context of the Christmas season, it is Jesus, the Word made flesh, who is shown as the light of all people (John 1:4).

The church's missionary impulse derives from the conviction that all are meant to share in the banquet of God's love. The Council asserted, "The Church's essential nature is universal . . . preaching the Word of God and proclaiming the kingdom throughout the whole world." (AG 1).

For This Week:

I want to remember:

I want to put my faith into action by:

Questions to Explore

Prayer for this Feast

God of light, unchanging Lord,
today you reveal to people of faith
the resplendent fact of the Word made flesh.
Your light is strong,
your love is near,
draw us beyond the limits which this world imposes,
to the life where your Spirit makes all life complete.
We ask this through Christ our Lord.

(Adapted from Evening Prayer for the feast of the Epiphany)

Baptism of the Lord

Scripture:

Isaiah 40:1-5, 9-11
Psalm 104:1b-2, 3-4, 24-25, 27-28, 29-30
Titus 2:11-14, 3:4-7
Luke 3:15-16, 21-22

Focus:

THE MEANING OF BAPTISM

Reflection Questions

1. *Name some ways you can integrate the life and mission of Jesus into your life.*

2. *What do you seek from the Holy Spirit as you prepare for baptism or the renewal of your baptismal commitment?*

Response

Directions: *Whether you are seeking baptism or desire to renew your baptismal commitment, in the space provided write your own baptismal prayer. In the prayer, express how you have experienced God's favor; ask God for the fullness of the Holy Spirit and name the ways you desire to fulfill your mission of discipleship in imitation of Jesus.*

Quotable Quotes

"Do you not know that all of us who have been baptized into Christ Jesus were baptized into his death? Therefore, we have been buried with him by baptism into death, so that, just as Christ was raised from the dead by the glory of the Father, so we too might walk in the newness of life."

(Romans 6:3-4 NRSV)

Did You Know?

Baptismal fonts come in varying shapes suggesting different effects. For example, there are cross-shaped fonts suggesting that the one being baptized is joined to the death of the Lord on the cross, rounded fonts to suggest the womb of mother Church giving birth to God's adopted children; there are octagonal fonts to suggest the "eighth day" of the Resurrection and our new creation; square fonts to suggest that Baptism is the door to new life and rectangular fonts suggesting a tomb in which we die with Christ to sin.

The Church Says:

John baptized Jesus in the Jordan, not because the Lord was sinful but because he wished to join himself to sinful humanity. This gesture of self-emptying is followed in all three synoptic gospels, Matthew, Mark and Luke, with the descent of the Holy Spirit and the voice of the Father, who declares, "You are my beloved Son." Similarly, baptism for the Christian celebrates God's favor and the infusion of the Spirit. Christian Baptism has two principal effects: purification from all sin and new birth in the Holy Spirit. Through baptism, all sins, original and personal, are forgiven. Through baptism all are incorporated into Christ as adopted children of God. As members of the Body of Christ, the baptized are members of one another. From the womb of the baptismal font is born the one people of God who transcend the natural human limits of nations, cultures, race and gender. Born of the font, enlightened by Christ and empowered by faith, believers walk as children of the light spreading the good news of salvation in their actions to assist the birth of the kingdom of God in the world.

For This Week:

I want to remember:

I want to put my faith into action by:

Questions to Explore

Prayer for this Feast

Jesus, Beloved of the Father,
enliven in us the desire
to fully live as your disciples.
Teach us the way of prayer.
Guide us with the presence
of your empowering Spirit.
Inspire us to bring the light of faith to the blind;
the freedom of forgiveness
to those who are imprisoned by hate;
and your liberating love
to those entrapped in the
dungeons of addiction.
May the baptismal waters become
living waters that will
quench our thirst for you and
drench the dryness of our lives.
Open us to the support and love of this faith community,
as we journey to you, the fountain of life.
Amen.

LENTEN SEASON

First Sunday of Lent

Scripture:

Deuteronomy 26:4-10
Psalm 91:1-2, 10-11, 12-13, 14-15
Romans 10:8-13
Luke 4:1-13

Focus:

WE ARE GOD'S CHOSEN PEOPLE.

Reflection

Directions: *As you reflect on today's gospel, allow the words to enter your heart. Respond to the passage by answering the questions that follow.*

Questions

1. *How have you, like the Israelites and Jesus, been tempted:*

    By hunger? *(the pursuit of those things which never satisfy)*

    By the lure of idolatry? *(the false gods which demand your time and energy)*

    By the temptation to test God? *(the ways we play god or push God to the limit)*

2. *When have you been able to resist these tests? What helped you overcome these basic urges?*

Did You Know?

"Desert" experiences are a well-known feature of the spiritual life, regarded as a time of spiritual testing. The desert fathers and mothers (late third and fourth centuries in Egypt and Palestine) were forerunners of monastic and hermetic life.

Lent originated as a time of baptismal renewal. Prayer, fasting and almsgiving are the three traditional Catholic practices during this season (Matthew 6:1-6,16-18).

The Church Says:

Jesus, in his humble submission to God's will, exemplifies for us the right response to divine election. It is not coincidental on this First Sunday of Lent when the Church celebrates God's election of catechumens, that we always read from a gospel account of the temptation of Jesus. Jesus' forty days in the desert echo Israel's testing for forty years. These gospel accounts tell of Jesus' unswerving trust and worship of a gracious and loving God. Thus God acts, God chooses, and in doing so, not only human pride is confounded but so too the pride of Satan is overturned. The entire life of Jesus, his ministry, suffering and death, points to God and God alone whose reign is overtaking this world. For in Christ, the faithful are gathered up, given membership in this kingdom and presented to God in a new and everlasting covenant.

Therefore, Catholic teaching emphasizes that the Church inherits Israel's election. While we regard the Jewish people as "chosen" (for how could God go back on his promise?), divine providence and grace is opened up in a new way by the coming of Christ. The Second Vatican Council chose to describe the Church as the "People of God." The Council proclaimed, "Christ instituted this new covenant, namely the new covenant in his blood (cf. 1 Corinthians 11:25); he called a race made up of Jews and Gentiles which would be one. . .and this race would be the new People of God (*Lumen Gentium*, 21 November 1964, n. 9).

For This Week:

I want to remember:

I want to put my faith into action by:

Questions to Explore

Prayer for the Week

God of Moses and Miriam,
you brought your chosen people out of the
bondage of slavery in Egypt.
Set me free.
God of the prophets,
you promised to set your people free from
the captivity of Babylon.
Make me aware of your promises in my life.
God of Joseph and Mary, through their 'yes,'
you offered your only Son, Jesus
to redeem us from the bondage of sin and death.
Open my eyes to see your covenant love.
God of the desert Fathers and Mothers,
you continually purify your church
through the spiritual renewal of these monastic ancestors.
Purify me and make of us a holy people.
Amen.

Second Sunday of Lent

Scripture:

Genesis 15:5-12, 17-18
Psalm 27:1, 7-8, 8-9, 13-14
Philippians 3:17-4:1 [or 3:20-4:1]
Luke 9:28b-36

Focus:

CONTEMPLATIVE PRAYER

Reflection

1. *Quiet yourself and take several deep breaths. Imagine the setting of the transfiguration. Visualize Jesus being transfigured. Then imagine yourself filled with this light of the transfigured Jesus. This is the same light that comes to us through baptism. Notice your feelings. Then, write several phrases about what happens to us when we are baptized.*

2. *Recall a powerful experience of God. In the space below describe what happened, the feelings you had, and the effect this experience had on you. With whom have you shared this experience?*

3. *Have you ever just sat in quiet prayer before God? When did you do this? Write four adjectives that describe your experience of quiet or contemplative prayer.*

Memorable People

St. Teresa of Avila, also called Teresa of Jesus, 1515-82, was a Carmelite nun and mystic well-known for her description of movements of prayer in "The Interior Castle." Her feast is celebrated on October 15.

St. John of the Cross, 1542-91, a mystical Doctor and joint founder of the Discalced Carmelites, was a contemporary of St. Teresa of Avila. His feast is celebrated December 14.

Bill Callahan of the Quixote Center wrote "Noisy Contemplation," a description of contemplative prayer available to the average person in his or her daily life.

Before his death, Anthony De Mello, S.J., wrote many books giving simple reflections and exercises for contemplative prayer.

Did You Know?

Religious communities are either apostolic, given to the spreading of the Gospel in the world, or contemplative. Religious men and women in contemplative orders spend much time in prayer. The best known contemplative orders are the Carthusian monks and nuns, and the Carmelite, Poor Clare, and some Dominican and Benedictine nuns.

Focusing on one's breath, or using a mantra, which is a simple word or phrase repeated over and over, e.g., "Lord Jesus, have mercy on me" is frequently used as a way to begin to experience contemplative prayer.

The Gospel of the transfiguration is used in each of the three years of readings on the second Sunday of Lent. The feast of the transfiguration is celebrated on August 6.

The Church Says:

Prayer is necessary as a way to communicate with and grow in relationship to God. There are many forms of prayer, from communal liturgical prayer to private prayer expressed in formulas or one's own words. A particular form of prayer, called contemplative prayer, has long been part of the church's tradition. Contemplative prayer is defined in different ways, though some common elements may be named. Contemplative prayer is a prayer of the heart that lifts one out of day-to-day concerns and brings an experience of connection with God. Contemplative prayer is more quiet than busy, and listens more than speaks words. Contemplative prayer may be described as a long, loving gaze at the beloved. There is a certain mystical quality to contemplative prayer, as portrayed in the experience of the disciples who were with Jesus transfigured.

Each person has his or her own style of prayer. There is no one right way to pray. The important thing is that the type and style of one's prayer is authentic and nurtures their relationship with God.

For This Week:

I want to remember:

I want to put my faith into action by:

Questions to Explore

Prayer for the Week

Pray a prayer of quiet for several minutes.

Let your mind rest.
Take several deep breaths,
and feel your breath come in and go out.
Visualize a light in your heart.
When your attention drifts,
return to the image of the light in your heart.
Feel its warmth and see its brightness.

When you sense you are finished,
pause and reflect on what you experienced.

Third Sunday of Lent

Scripture:

Exodus 3:1-8a, 13-15
Psalm 103: 1-2, 3-4, 6-7, 8, 11
1 Corinthians 10:1-6, 10-12
Luke 13:1-9

Focus:

THE LORD IS KIND AND MERCIFUL.

Reflection

Directions: *Recall your personal experiences of God from childhood to the present day. List several of these in the space provided by using a phrase of short sentence that triggers the memory. Look over this list and choose two or three of these experiences of God. Base your selection upon the quality of God's mercy, love and kindness revealed to you in the experience. Allow these memories of God to linger for a few moments before you respond to the questions.*

Questions

1. *What did you discover in your personal experiences of God's mercy, love and kindness?*

2. *What response do you wish to make for this kind and merciful God?*

3. *How will you experience of God's mercy and kindness change the way you treat others?*

Quotable Quotes

"Remove the sandals from your feet,
for the place on which you are standing
is holy ground." (Exodus 3:5)

Did You Know?

God's self naming as "I am who am" in this week's reading from Exodus 3:14 is well-known. John's Gospel gives seven "I am" descriptions of Jesus, thus connecting Jesus, God's Word, with God. Jesus is known as: the bread of life, the living water, the way the truth and the life, the good shepherd, the sheep gate, the light of the world, and the resurrection and the life.

Moses hid his face from God (Exodus 3:6) because of the belief that no one could see God's face and live.

The Church Says:

Many different qualities are associated with God. The church knows God to be a kind and merciful God. God is gracious, loving and wants good for all people. God's mercy is beyond our imagining. God does not seek "an eye for an eye or a tooth for a tooth." Rather, God shows compassion, understanding the struggles of the human heart. The people of Israel in their understanding of God moved from having many gods, to belief in the one, true God. The "I am who am" God of Israel established a covenant with humankind. Through this personal, covenantal relationship, the Chosen People grew in their understanding of God. They moved from a transcendent, all powerful, unapproachable concept of God to coming to know God as a close, caring, presence who loves and shows mercy. The God whom Jesus proclaimed is consistently a God of kindness and mercy whose love is beyond all telling.

For This Week:

I want to remember:

I want to put my faith into action by:

Questions to Explore

Prayer for the Week

God of life, you are good and holy,
slow to anger and rich in kindness,
merciful and always forgiving.
May I know and trust
your love for me more each day.
Help me let down my guard with you
and not be afraid
to show you may face and heart.
You are the holy one of my life. Amen.

Fourth Sunday of Lent

Scripture:

Joshua 5:9a, 10-12
Psalm 34:2-3, 4-5, 6-7
2 Corinthians 5:17-21
Luke 15:1-3, 11-32

Focus:

CONVERSION

Reflection

Directions: *Recall a time when you needed God's total forgiveness. Write that experience and its effects upon your life. Be sure to include the situation, the people involved and your feelings before and after the experience of God's forgiveness.*

Questions

1. *How has God's forgiveness changed you in a significant or even a radical way?*

2. *Did you ever share that experience with another? What was their reaction?*

Memorable People

Christians have cherished down through the ages the autobiographical work of St. Augustine, *The Confessions*, which detail his journey away from sin and toward God. In 1948, Thomas Merton told the story of his journey to Catholic faith and monastic life in his autobiography, *The Seven Story Mountain*. The book was a bestseller and continues to inspire readers today. Contemporary movies, such as *Romero* and *Dead Man Walking*, have also tackled the subject of conversion.

Did You Know?

During the Vietnam war, American POWs copied in secret portions of the Bible, since books were denied to them except for Christmas day. They used toilet tissue for paper, wire for pens, and ashes for ink. The passages they recorded were the Lost Sheep, and the most famous of all Jesus' parables: the Prodigal Son (Mark Link, *Path Through Scripture*, Thomas More, Allen, Texas, 1987, p. 137).

The Church Says:

Jesus begins his public ministry with the call to repent and believe in the good news (Matthew 4:17 and Mark 1:15). Jesus preaches conversion. The imperative to change one's life in accord with the life of God is not simply meant for those who are hearing the gospel for the first time in preparation for baptism. Catholic theology has always recognized conversion as an on-going reality after one's baptism.

Conversion is not only an individual task but is an invitation for communities and groups to pursue, since sinfulness and the tendency toward sin can also be experienced within, imbedded in and practiced by those communities and groups. John Paul II has devoted a significant portion of his apostolic exhortation "Reconciliation and Penance" (2 December 1984, n 16) to an exposition of the social aspects of sin and the resulting need for conversion by groups.

The inner conversion called for by Jesus and for which all constantly strive is expressed eventually in outward signs and gestures. The radical reorienting of one's life issues forth in good works.

For This Week:

I want to remember:

I want to put my faith into action by:

Questions to Explore

Prayer for the Week

*God, open my heart to change;
    turn my selfishness to generosity,
    turn my prejudice to acceptance;
    turn my fear to faith;
turn around my whole life.
Let me not hold back anything from your
    nurturing, forgiving and reconciling love
Create in me a desire to take this Good News
    of your forgiveness to others.
Create in me a willingness to be your
    ambassador in the Way of Jesus. Amen*

Fifth Sunday of Lent

Scripture:

Isaiah 43:16-21
Psalm 126:1-2, 2-3, 4-5, 6
Philippians 3:8-14
John 8:1-11

Focus:

RECONCILIATION

Reflection

Directions: *Think about these attitudes of heart, taken from this week's Scriptures, in your own life. Which ones do you harbor in your heart? You may wish to make these with a check or circle. When you have finished reflecting upon the list, create another list of attitudes of the heart which you ask God to implant in your heart. Close this time of reflection with a prayer asking God to create something new in you.*

Attitudes of the Heart (for which you repent)

quick to judge
self-righteousness
distrust the motives of others
inability to forgive
stuck in the past
resistance to change
fear of being 'found out'
unfaithful in relationships with others
unfaithful to God
desirous of vengeance

Attitudes of the Heart (which you desire)

Quotable Quotes

"We entreat you on behalf of Christ,
be reconciled to God."
(2 Corinthians 5:20)

Did You Know?

Baptism is the primary sacrament of reconciliation. Early Christians, those who committed the grave sins of murder, adultery and apostasy (publicly denying one's faith) after their baptism were reconciled to the community only after years of public penance. The public sinner was required to stand outside the church in sack cloth and ashes as the rest of the community assembled for Eucharist.

The Church Says:

The victory of Jesus Christ over sin is first actualized for believers in baptism where our fallen nature is crucified with Christ so that we might be freed from the slavery of sin and rise with Christ to live with God (Romans 6:4-10). We are claimed for Christ in baptism and are incorporated into the Church, his body. Thus we are made members of this ecclesial communion and belong to one another.

Those who fall into sin after baptism experience the forgiveness of God in the sacrament of Reconciliation. The healing effected by the celebration of this sacrament also restores one's relationship with the Church. To be reconciled to God means to also be reconciled with God's Church.

Reconciliation does not mean merely being detached from sin. The healing brought about by the sacrament and the forgiveness experienced in reconciliation works a real change in the person. With the remission of sins, there is, at the same time, the sanctification and renewal of the inner person. As the reconciled sinner is released from the bondage of sin, that individual is free to live anew in the light of God's grace.

For This Week:

I want to remember:

I want to put my faith into action by:

Questions to Explore

Prayer for the Week

Lord Jesus Christ,
you are the Lamb of God;
you take away the sins of the world.
Through the grace of the Holy Spirit
restore me to friendship with our Father,
cleanse me from every stain of sin
in the blood you shed for me,
and raise me to new life
for the glory of your name.
(Rite of Penance, n 91)

Palm Sunday of the Lord's Passion

Scripture:

Isaiah 50:4-7
Psalm 22:7-8, 16-17, 18-19, 22-23
Philippians 2:6-11
Luke 22:14-23:56 [or 23:1-49]

Focus:

THE MEANING OF SUFFERING

Reflection

Directions: *Enter the passion of Jesus by assuming the place of one of the characters who witnessed Jesus' suffering: Simon, one of the women of Jerusalem, the repentant criminal who crucified with Jesus, the centurion, Joseph of Arimathea or one of the women at the foot of the cross. Imagine the scene of his suffering and death through the eyes of this character. In the space below write your reflection naming your emotions, your thoughts and your response to the call to join with Christ's saving actions.*

Questions

1. *What insights did you gain from this meditation?*

2. *How can your current suffering or pain be transformed through union with Christ's passion?*

Quotable Quotes

When the centurion saw what had taken place,
he praised God and said,
"Certainly this man was innocent."
(Luke 23:47)

Did You Know?

The stigmata (from Latin for "marks") are bodily signs of Christ's passion. St. Paul refers to carrying the "marks" of the Lord Jesus (Galatians 6:17). The most notable stigmatic was St. Francis of Assisi, who experienced the wound marks of Jesus in 1224, two years before his death. Stigmata may be visible or, as in the case of St. Catherine of Sienna, invisible. Rarely does the Church accept as authentic a case of the stigmata, and has not attempted to define how they occur.

The Church Says:

For the five weeks of the Lenten season the Church prepares by works of love and self-sacrifice to celebrate the Lord's paschal mystery, his suffering, death and resurrection. Today's feast celebrates how the Messiah accomplished our salvation through this passover from death to new life. Following Christ in faith, the Church professes that if we are united with the Lord in his suffering on the cross, we too will share in his resurrection and new life. From that union is derived the Christian understanding of pain and suffering.

Sickness, pain and suffering are burdens shared by everyone to greater or lesser degrees. In the light of faith, these burdens are given significance. For St. Paul, the passover effected by the suffering, death and resurrection of Jesus is the basic pattern of all redemption. He goes so far as to say that believers must be ready to fill up what is lacking in Christ's sufferings for the salvation of the world (Colossians 1:24). St. Paul also reminds the Corinthian community that believers continually carry within their own bodies the dying of Jesus, so that in our bodies the life of Jesus may also be revealed. (2 Corinthians 4:10) The dying of Jesus that Paul asks us to embrace is more than a metaphor.

Affirming the value and significance of human suffering does not mean, however, that we are not to fight against illness or do nothing to alleviate conditions of misery, suffering and pain. In his earthly ministry, Jesus had compassion on those who were sick and worked miracles of healing. As disciples who continue the ministry of Jesus, we owe those who are suffering as much physical relief and spiritual comfort as we can possibly provide.

For This Week:

I want to remember:

I want to put my faith into action by:

Questions to Explore

Prayer for the Week

O God, help us put on the attitude of Christ,
Take the sorrows of our lives
transform them with your joy;
Take the chaos of our lives
transform them with your calm;
Take the humiliations we have experienced
transform them with your glory;
Take the adversities of our lives
transform them with your strength;
Take our mourning and weeping
transform them with your consolation.
O God, Our God, rouse us to willingly empty ourselves
that we might be filled with
the glory of the Risen One. Amen.

EASTER SEASON

Scripture:

Acts 10:34a, 37-43
Psalm 118:1-2, 16-17, 22-23
Colossians 3:1-4 or 1 Corinthians 5:6b-8
John 20:1-9

Focus:

THE RESURRECTION OF JESUS

Reflection Poem

This poem is helpful in the struggle to understand the full impact of resurrection on our lives. Take time to read it thoughtfully and then respond to the questions listed.

An Easter Meditation
by the Rev. Patrick Mooney

All seems hopeless
Life seems to life
Only to fall
Like withered fruit or flowers
Unto the ground

But Jesus Lord
I really believe
Just because there is a hill
Which blocks my vision
I cannot say
A valley does not run
Beyond that hill

And just because
The day is dark
I cannot say
The sun does not shine
Beyond the clouds

Easter teaches
Tenacity breeds triumph
And resurrection is for those
Who dare to wait
Like patient bulbs
Beneath the winter crust

Paradoxically
Faith is greatest
When it springs from ruins
The flower more beautiful
When touched by rain

And the tree more bent with fruit
When pruned and pinched
By a cutting knife

Possibilities are stressed
By their opposite
The dark accentuates the light

And the foulness of cruel Calvary's deed
Becomes the seed
For Easter hope

Because of you Christ
Death is only an appearance
Limited by my feeble sight
But I believe despite the shadows
That spring sprouts eternal from the grave

Tombs become wombs
For those who surrender
To mystery . . .

Mooney, Rev. Patrick, "An Easter Meditation,"
Religion Teachers Journal, March 1978, p.9.

Questions

1. *What images in the poem did you find inspiring?*

2. *After reflecting on this poem, how would you describe resurrection?*

The Church Says:

The chains of death are truly broken. Just as the divine nature took on our humanity (in all things but sin), so too the resurrection of Jesus was accomplished in a real human body. The risen Lord is not a ghost who returns to haunt the disciples, nor some sort of resuscitated corpse. The resurrection of Jesus is a passing over from death into a new life, a new existence.

That Jesus rose from the dead is an actual, historical event and not a psychological or spiritual experience of the disciples. This is not some myth or wish-fulfillment on their part, or ours. Those first disciples witnessed something totally unexpected and surprising and which they only gradually understood. And in understanding it, they were willing to be martyred in telling the good news of the resurrection

The implications for us believers is that by the resurrection God ratifies Jesus' whole life and teaching. Baptized into his death by our plunging beneath the waters of the font, we rise as adopted children of God whose inheritance is the resurrection. Even now we taste the promise of new, risen life in the Eucharist.

For This Week:

I want to remember:

I want to put my faith into action by:

Questions to Explore

Prayer for the Week

Let my voice join with
all of creation,
Jesus Christ is Risen, Alleluia!
With the winds of spring
I praise the Risen Christ
You have truly risen, Alleluia!

Let my head nod with the lilies,
daffodils, tulips and trees,
Christ has overcome death, Alleluia!

In the fullness of the sun's light
dawning on yet another festival of hope,
I join with all of heaven and earth
in the song of gladness
Christ is risen, Alleluia!
I, too, rise with him, Alleluia!

Second Sunday of Easter

Scripture:

Acts 5:12-16
Psalm 118:2-4, 13-15, 22-24
Revelation 1:9-11a, 12-13, 17-19
John 20:19-31

Focus:

FAITH

Reflection

Directions: *In the space below, list some of your current fears. Then beside these fears list the assurances of faith found in today's Scripture passages.*

FEARS   ASSURANCE OF FAITH

Questions

1. *How is your faith supported in the community walking with you in your journey of conversion?*

2. *What trials and difficulties have caused you to doubt? How was your faith restored? Write your story of faith in the space below.*

Quotable Quotes

"Blessed are those
who have not seen
and yet have come to believe."

(John 20:29)

Did You Know?

There are several Hebrew words for faith, all of which refer to something "solid" or "trustworthy," to which we pledge our loyalty. Our word "amen" comes from a Hebrew word for faith *(aman)*. From this perspective, faith is understood as "I believe you," a relationship of trust.

The Church Says:

Faith invites us into a relationship of love, for "God is love." The hidden, triune God is fully revealed in Jesus Christ, who embodies divine love and who communicates that love to us by his life and mission and by his suffering, death and resurrection. That divine love is freely given, and our free response is how Catholic teaching describes "faith." The gift of faith is therefore a relationship wherein we trust the truth of that which has been revealed in Jesus Christ, handed down by those first witnesses, and afterwards, from generation to generation in the church.

A heritage of faith is entrusted to the whole church. The Catholic genius understands this sacred deposit, this inheritance, as contained in both Scripture and Tradition. Indeed, the development of the New Testament shows the process of the living Tradition at work. The function of authoritative church teaching is to explain and guard this "deposit of faith."

Our relationship to God in faith can be shaken. We experience evil, suffering and injustice in this world, and we question God, we doubt, and we struggle in our belief. In times of doubt and struggle, individuals can turn to the community of faith for support.

For This Week:

I want to remember:

I want to put my faith into action by:

Questions to Explore

Prayer for the Week

Loving and faithful God,
thank you for the gift of faith.
I want to believe in you
with all of my heart and soul.
Deepen and grow the seeds of faith in me
that the roots of my flowering faith
might be strengthened
to overcome any weeds of doubt
Open my eyes to see you in all things
during these times of doubt ad trouble.
You have graciously gifted me
with this community of faith
o support and nourish the seed of faith
you have planted in my soul.
May your Spirit breath upon me
and empower me to support and encourage
this gift of faith in others. Amen

Third Sunday of Easter

Scripture:

Acts 5:27-32, 40b-41
Psalm 30:2, 4, 5-6, 11-12, 13
Revelation 5:11-14
John 21:1-19 [or John 21:1-4]

Focus:

EUCHARIST CALLS US TO MISSION.

Reflection

Directions: *Reflect upon the gospel narrative, particularly on the three-fold challenge to the disciples: 1) Jesus tells his followers where and how to catch the fish; 2) the shared meal is a result of the combined work of Jesus (the bread) and the disciples (the fish) and is offered in humble service; and 3) the challenge to "Feed my sheep" results in suffering and even death. Reflect upon these three movements in the narrative and then write your own thoughts defining the challenge the Lord presents to you as his follower.*

CATCHING FISH

SHARING THE MEAL

FEEDING SHEEP AND SUFFERING

Questions

1. *Recall a time when you acted as part of God's mission. What did you say or do? What effect did this have on you and others?*

2. *Who, from among your immediate relationships, is in need of being fed, physically and/or spiritually? Name some of the people in your family or church who would be willing to share this mission with you.*

Quotable Quotes

Paul VI in his encyclical letter on evangelization, reminds the Church of the connection between celebrating the sacraments and spreading the good news. He tells us to live "the sacraments as true sacraments of faith—and not to receive them passively or to undergo them." (*Evangelii Nuntiandi*, n. 47)

Did You Know?

In 1951, director Mervin LeRoy made a film of the popular novel *Quo Vadis* by the Polish author Henryk Sienkiewicz (1896). As Peter is fleeing the persecutions of Nero, Jesus appears to him and the disciple asks "Lord, where are you going?" Jesus replies, "To Rome, to be crucified a second time." Peter returns to Rome to be martyred. This legend is preserved in a small church on the Via Appia Antica near the catacombs of St. Sebastian. In it is a replica shown to visitors of a stone supposedly impressed with Christ's footprints. (*Rome*, Knopf Guides, Alfred A. Knopf Inc., 1994, p 324-25.)

The Church Says:

Discipleship does not turn in upon itself. By its nature, Christian discipleship is a following of Jesus who calls us to join him in carrying the cross and witnessing to the good news of the kingdom of God. Discipleship thus leads to the Eucharist, the meal of the sacrifice of Jesus and, in turn, this meal leads us to evangelize.

Catholics believe that the Eucharist is the foundational sacrament which makes us who we are as a Church. The Second Vatican Council describes the Eucharist as "the source and summit of the Christian life." Those who join together in the celebration of the Eucharist not only offer to God the sacrifice of Christ but offer themselves and their lives in union with the Savior. Indeed, it is our Catholic understanding of this sacrament that it brings to perfection all the gifts offered and all the sacrifices made by us for the kingdom of God.

For This Week:

I want to remember:

I want to put my faith into action by:

Questions to Explore

Prayer for the Week

Risen Jesus, you shared yourself
with your companions in the
bread and fish on the beach.
I long to share your meal of love
with you and my companions
on this my journey of faith.
Nourish me to share this food
with those in the world, who
hunger for you.
Open me to the mission as your disciple
in spite of any suffering it may
bring my way.
Prepare my heart to receive you,
the risen one. Amen.

Fourth Sunday of Easter

Scripture:

Acts 13:14, 43-52
Psalm 100:1-2, 3, 5
Revelation 7:9, 14b-17
John 10:27-30

Focus:

THE DIVINITY OF CHRIST

Reflection

Directions: *Recall the images of the Good Shepherd, using the poster board or paper created in the Dismissal Session as a reminder. Reflect on how God has been your Good Shepherd—SAFE PASTURE, PROTECTION, GUIDANCE, ETERNAL LIFE, PROVIDENTIAL CARE—what would you add. In the space below, write your experiences in which God acted as a Good Shepherd in your life. Be sure to include how you have heard the voice of the Good Shepherd.*

Questions

1. *How is God's promise of eternal life transforming you?*

2. *What could possibly snatch us from the hand of the shepherd?*

3. *Who is this Jesus, the Good Shepherd?*

Quotable Quotes

"There was a great multitude that no one could count, from every nation, from all tribes and peoples and languages, standing before the throne and before the Lamb, robed in white, with palm branches in their hands . . . Who are these, robed in white, and where have they come from? . . . These are they who have come out of the great ordeal; they have washed their robes and made them white in the blood of the Lamb."

(Revelation 7:9, 13, 14)

Did You Know?

The earliest paintings of Jesus are of the image of a shepherd holding a sheep on his shoulders. These are found in the catacombs of St. Callistus and St. Priscilla in Rome. The bishop of a diocese is known as the "chief shepherd" of the local church. His crosier, or staff, is modeled on a shepherd's crook.

The Church Says:

Jesus' statement that "The Father and I are one" (John 10:30) can be understood as a scriptural basis for our belief in Christ's divinity. By the time of the Council of Nicea in 325, the doctrine of the Trinity, that there are three equal persons (God the Father, Son, and Holy Spirit) in one God, was clearly stated. The Council went on to define that Jesus is of the same substance as God, and was eternally "begotten," not made. This understanding of Christ was challenged, but remained and is described as the most fundamental and essential teaching in the Catholic Church. In our Catholic practice, we acknowledge the divinity of Christ by giving him worship, as contrasted with the saints whom we honor. We state this belief in Christ's divinity when we say the Creed. During the Preparation of Gifts at Mass, the belief in Christ's divinity is expressed in the words stated by the presider: "By the mystery of this water and wine may we come to share in the divinity of Christ, who humbled himself to share in our humanity." (Order of Mass, *Roman Missal*)

For This Week:

I want to remember:

I want to put my faith into action by:

Questions to Explore

Prayer for the Week

Lord Jesus, human and divine,
you are my shepherd.
You are all I have and need.
You bring me to streams of
life-giving water.
You refresh my soul.
You are always there to guide me,
through every dark valley and
in the face of every evil.
May I always hear your voice,
and follow you all the days of my life. Amen.

Scripture:

Acts 14:21-27
Psalm 145:8-9, 10-11, 12-13
Revelation 21:1-5a
John 13:31-33a, 34-35

Focus:

THE LAW OF LOVE

Reflection

Directions: *Christ has first loved us, and asks us to become a fuller part of him in loving one another. State what you need from God to truly love all people.*

Name the people who have truly loved you. Next to their names write down the feelings or qualities their love evoked in you. How were you changed by their love? Let yourself feel Christ's love for you. How are you changed by this love?

Quotable Quotes

"Then I saw a new heaven and a new earth; ...And I saw the holy city, the new Jerusalem, coming down out of heaven from God, prepared as a bride adorned for her husband...And the one who was seated on the throne said, "See, I am making all things new." Revelation 21:1, 2, 5

"Beloved, let us love one another, because love is from God; everyone who loves is born of God and knows God. Whoever does not love does not know God, for God is love." (1 John 4:7-8)

"Beloved, since God loved us so much, we also ought to love one another. No one has ever seen God; if we love one another, God lives in us. (1 John 4:11-12)

Memorable People

In 1633, St. Vincent de Paul and Louise de Marillac founded a religious community of women, the Daughters of Charity, who worked directly among the poor. In 1809, St. Elizabeth Ann Seton, the first person born in the United States ever to be canonized (1975), began an American community, the Sisters of Charity, out of the spirit of St. Vincent de Paul.

Did You Know?

At the Evening Mass of the Lord's Supper, the Church proclaims the passage from John's gospel of Jesus washing the disciples feet (John 13:1-15), and includes a ritual action of washing feet at the Mass. This action of washing feet, which gives expression to the love Christ calls us to live, is called in Latin, the *"mandatum"* (commandment) from *"Mandatum novum do vobis"* or "I give you a new commandment.")

The Church Says:

The Law of Moses structured relationships in society. For example, lying, stealing and adultery were forbidden by the ten commandments. The law of love is also found in the old covenant. In Deuteronomy 6:5, people are told to love God wholly and completely, and in Leviticus 19:18, people are exhorted to love your neighbor as yourself. Jesus calls the commandment to love a "new" commandment. The new law of Jesus opens believers to the full potential of that first covenant. The new commandment of love is etched upon your hearts not only by pondering scripture, but by partaking of the living tradition of discipleship through the outpouring of the Spirit in Christ. This commandment is also new because it derives its meaning from example and love of Jesus. He showed us this love through his examples in the many events of his life, by washing the disciples' feet, and later by dying on the cross. Eucharist, as presented in John's gospel, is the meal which symbolizes our following in the way of love, the way of service and sacrifice for one another. Loving one another is the sign by which we are known as Christ's disciples.

For This Week:

I want to remember:

I want to put my faith into action by:

Questions to Explore

Prayer for the Week

Let yourself become quiet.

Take several breaths in and out.

Picture yourself surrounded by God's love.

Let the word "love" form in you as you breathe in, and "use me" form in you as you breathe out.

Continue this prayer for five to ten minutes.

Then reflect on what you experienced in this prayer.

Sixth Sunday of Easter

Scripture:

Acts 15:1-2, 22-29
Psalm 67:2-3, 5, 6, 8
Revelation 21:10-14, 22-23
John 14:23-29

Focus:

PEACE

Reflection

NEW JERUSALEM, KINGDOM OF PEACE

"Then I saw a new heaven and a new earth; for the first heaven and the first earth had passed away, and the sea was no more. And I saw the holy city, the new Jerusalem, coming down out of heaven from God, prepared as a bride adorned for her husband. And I heard a loud voice from the throne saying, "See, the home of God is among mortals. He will dwell with them as their God; they will be his peoples, and God himself will be with them; he will wipe every tear from their eyes. Death will be no more; mourning and crying and pain will be no more, for the first things have passed away." *(Revelation 21:1-4)*

As you ponder this image from John's writing in the Book of Revelation, imagine your own sense of this ultimate vision—a new Jerusalem, a kingdom of peace. Then respond to the following questions

Questions

1. *How would you describe and characterize your dream?*

2. *Using the fullness of the meaning of peace, flowing from the covenant with God (see the newsprint), how would peace be lived out in this new Jerusalem?*

3. *What would you change about your life, today, to bring about this peaceable kingdom?*

Quotable Quotes

In the words of *The Challenge of Peace:*
"Peacemaking is not an optional commitment. It is a requirement of our faith. We are called to be peacemakers, not by some movement of the moment, but by our Lord Jesus.
The content and context of our peacemaking is set not by some political agenda or ideological program, but by the teaching of his Church."

Did You Know?

Rich with symbolism, the new Jerusalem is a perfect cube, like the holy of holies in the Temple. With its twelve gates (signifying the twelve tribes of Israel, the twelve apostles, and fullness generally), and its illumination from within by the divine presence, it symbolizes all the beauty and perfection of the Church.

The Church Says:

Pope John's message, and the Catholic understanding of peace, begin with Jesus farewell gift to his disciples. Jesus speaks the word "peace" in the context of a biblical understanding of "shalom." The Hebrew "shalom," found in the Old Testament, means much more than the absence of war or maintaining a balance of power. "Shalom" means the well-being of daily life, a total harmony with nature, God and self. It issues forth from justice and is experienced in a fruitful land and people, who have plentiful food, and dwell in security, free from fear. "Shalom" is the sum of all the benefits of God's presence with his people. Jesus gives this gift of peace in the widest sense possible. Peace is the fruit of the covenant between God and believers. Those who follow the light of Jesus as disciples walk the paths of peace and know from his teaching that "blessed are the peacemakers." (Matthew 5:9)

For This Week:

I want to remember:

I want to put my faith into action by:

Questions to Explore

Prayer for this Feast

O Prince of Peace
may your covenant of love
beat our swords and weapons of war
into plowshares and shovels

Make of us a peace loving people
disarmed and vulnerable
with open hearts and homes for those
caught up in the wars of ideas
ideals, intimacy and identity.

Let us not lust for power over
But the harmony found in empowerment.

Let us not horde our rich gifts
But use them to bring about the new Jerusalem.
Make us adventurers and peacemakers in this
chaotic world. Amen.

Seventh Sunday of Easter

Scripture:

Acts 7:55-60
Psalm 97:1-2, 6-7, 9
Revelation 22:12-14, 16-17, 20
John 17:20-26

Focus:

CHRISTIAN UNITY

Worksheet

1. *From the Revelation reading, describe the vision and how Jesus is portrayed. How does this vision affect you?*

2. *In Jesus' farewell discourse he prays "that all may be one." What is he saying by this? Give meaning and examples.*

3. *What is the hope for those who choose to follow Christ?*

4. *Reflect on your experiences of oneness with family members, friends, God. Recall a specific time you felt at one with God and others. Write that experience in the space provided.*

Memorable People

Pope John XXIII was regarded as a strong advocate for ecumenism, and the council he convened (Vatican II) did much to promote church unity. Rumor has it that his dying words were *"ut unum sint"* (that they may be one).

Did You Know?

A Week of Prayer for Christian Unity, begun in the Anglican Communion in 1908, is celebrated by Catholics (and other Christian churches) in January, culminating on January 25, the feast of the conversion of St. Paul, and in some countries around Pentecost. Lewis Thomas Wattson, who began this week of prayer, also founded with Lurana Mary White a Franciscan community called the Society of the Atonement, in Graymoor, New York and were received into the Roman Catholic church in 1909. The Society of the Atonement continues to promote Christian Unity through the Week of Prayer, publications, and the work of their members. At the opening of the Easter Vigil, the wax of the paschal candle—a symbol of Christ—is etched with an Alpha and an Omega, recalling today's reading from Revelation.

The Church Says:

Unity is a gift given to the Church by Christ. Its source is the Trinity, the union of God, one in three. The gift of unity does not mean uniformity. From its beginning, the church has been characterized by a great diversity of gifts. The church continues to struggle with the divisions and separations that exists in the Christian church. A drive toward ecumenism began before Vatican II. In 1949, the Holy Office issued an instruction endorsing Catholic participation in conferences whose aim was the promotion of ecumenism. Ecumenism was one of the four principal goals of Vatican II. With the publication of the Decree of Ecumenism in 1964 (*unitatis Redintegratio*) the Catholic Church became irrevocably committed to ecumenism. This decree states clearly that many of the significant elements which build up and give life to the household of God can and do exist "outside the visible boundaries of the Catholic Church" (UR 3). The ecumenical movement has impelled Catholics, Orthodox and Protestants to join together in prayer, good works, study and dialogue. In 1995, John Paul II issued an encyclical letter, *"Ut Unum Sint"* in which he urges common prayer, spiritual renewal and conversion with the hope of movement toward one Christian family. (UUS, 42.1)

For This Week:

I want to remember:

I want to put my faith into action by:

Questions to Explore

Prayer for the Week

God of love, you desire that all of your people be united in your love. Let me see all of my sisters and brothers with your eyes. Let me see their goodness and struggles. Make me slow to judge. Help me bring about the oneness you desire through my words and actions. Remind me often that we are all one in you, our source of life. I pray in love and in trust. Amen.

Pentecost

Scripture:

Acts 2:1-11
Psalm 104:1, 24, 29-30, 31, 34
1 Corinthians 12:3b-7, 12-13
John 20:19-23

Focus:

THE GIFTS OF THE SPIRIT AND THE SACRAMENT OF CONFIRMATION

Worksheet

1. *What does the gift of the Holy Spirit mean for us as a people today?*

2. *Where are the places in your neighborhoods, city, state, world, that cry out for the Spirit of hope?*

3. *Where in your own life do you need to break through to a new horizon of the power of the Spirit?*

Quotable Quotes

"All powerful God, Father of our Lord Jesus Christ, by water and the Holy Spirit you freed your sons and daughters from sin and gave them new life. Send your Holy Spirit upon them to be their helper and guide. Give them the spirit of wisdom and understanding, the spirit of right judgment and courage, the spirit of knowledge and reverence. Fill them with the spirit of wonder and awe in your presence . . .

(Rite of Confirmation, 25)

Memorable People

St. Ambrose admonished those confirmed, "Guard what you have received. God the Father has marked you with his sign: Christ the Lord has confirmed you and has placed his pledge, the Spirit, in your hearts."
(De myst. 7, 42: PL 16, 402-403).

Did You Know?

In the early history of the Church, the laying on of hands was recognized as the origin of the sacrament of Confirmation. An anointing with chrism (perfumed oil) on the forehead was soon added to the laying on of hands. The designation "Christian" means "anointed."

Since the New Testament reports that the Spirit descended upon Jesus as a dove (Mark 1:10), artists have depicted the Holy Spirit as a dove. This dove symbol is common in catacombs and on early Christian sarcophagi (burial containers).

The Church Says:

Pentecost Sunday, which concludes the fifty days of the Easter Season, celebrates the conferral of the Holy Spirit upon the gathered apostles and Mary. The Sacrament of Confirmation perpetuates this grace by which new members of the church are sealed with the gift of the Spirit. Catholic teaching emphasizes that those confirmed are sealed in the Lord and cannot be confirmed again. When baptized as an infant, Confirmation is celebrated later when they are able to understand this sacrament. Confirmation remains a sealing of the Baptism. The Spirit is already received at Baptism. The laying on of hands was the origin of the Sacrament, and took place immediately after the Baptism of adults when the Bishop was present. The oil has meanings of joy, abundance, limbering, healing, soothing, and sealing. Oil cannot be easily removed.

The Spirit continues to be active in continuing the mission of Christ in the world. The presence of the Spirit can be known by its fruits: love, joy, peace, patience, kindness, generosity, faithfulness, gentleness, and self-control. (Galatians 5:22-23)

For This Week:

I want to remember:

I want to put my faith into action by:

Questions to Explore

Prayer for the Week

God of light, send your Spirit into my life with the power of a mighty wind, and by the flame of your wisdom open the horizon of my mind. Loosen my tongue to sing your praise in words beyond the power of speech. Continue to work through me and the hearts of all who believe. Amen.

ORDINARY TIME

Scripture:

Isaiah 62:1-5
Psalm 96:1-2, 2-3, 7-8, 9-10
1 Corinthians 12:4-11
John 2:1-11

Focus:

SACRAMENT OF MARRIAGE

Reflection

Directions: *Characterize marital love in action through your observations/personal experiences of spousal love. Create a list below:*

From your list make direct and specific statements characterizing God's love for all people. Use the format, "God's love is _____"

Questions

From this concrete exercise:

1. *What did you discover about your relationship with God?*

2. *How can God's love 'grace' your marital relationship and/or friendships?*

3. *What gifts do you bring for the harmony and common good in your relationships?*

4. *How does God's faithful love bring about 'miracles' in the most ordinary circumstances?*

Memorable People

While there are few married saints celebrated in the Church calendar, St. Margaret of Scotland, found time to be a wife, queen, mother and saint. Raising her six children, and working with her husband King Malcolm, together, the couple found time every day to rise early to prepare breakfast for the hundreds of beggars that gathered outside the castle each day.

Did You Know?

Norwegian Catholic author, Sigrid Undset (1882-1949), who won the Nobel Prize in 1928, wrote *Kristen Lavrensdatter*, a three-volume epic of a woman's life and faith, set in medieval Norway. Kristen's marriage plays a central role in the novels, which enjoyed great popularity among generations of Catholic readers and has never been out of print since its first publication in 1927.

The Church Says:

Marriage is part of God's plan. The Old Testament scriptures speak eloquently about marriage and the love of a husband and wife enshrined in that marital institution. With the coming of Christ, however, God in Jesus raised the marital covenant between baptized persons to the dignity of a sacrament (CCC 1601). This Sunday's gospel account reports how Jesus works his first sign, changing water into wine, at a wedding feast. By his presence at the wedding at Cana, the Church understands Jesus' confirming the innate goodness of love in marriage. Thus, marriage becomes an effective sign of Christ's presence (CCC 1613).

John Paul II, taking up themes taught by the Second Vatican Council, elaborates on the characteristics of conjugal love. In his apostolic exhortation, Familiaris Consortio (22 November 1981), he further clarifies the teaching of the Council, describing the love between husband and wife as involving a totality of body, instinct, power, emotion, and aspiration of the spirit and will aiming at a deeply personal unity which goes beyond union in one flesh to encompass the formation of one heart and soul (FC, 19). This is, in part, offered as a rationale which demands the indissolubility of marriage (CCC 1643). The Council itself had stipulated that along with the mutual self-giving of the two partners, the other end of marriage is the education and rearing of children (Gaudium et Spes, 7 December 1965, n 48).

For This Week:

I want to remember:

I want to put my faith into action by:

Questions to Explore

Prayer for the Week

Creator of love, it is you who first loved us
making it possible for us to love
one another, in spite of our humanness.
Bless the love between couples everywhere.
Embrace them, sending your Spirit
of gentleness and affection;
of joy and playfulness;
of tenderness and compassion°.
That through the love of mere humans
You might renew the earth
By changing
our watered-down humanness
into the flavorful, full bodied wine
of your deep love.

Third Sunday in Ordinary Time

Scripture:

Nehemiah 8:2-4, 5-6, 8-10
Psalm 19:8, 9, 10, 15
1 Corinthians 12:12-30 [or 12:12-14, 27]
Luke 1:1-4; 4:14-21

Focus:

SACRED SCRIPTURE

Reflection

Directions: *Read slowly and ponder today's readings.*

Questions

1. *Name one or two Bible stories that are your favorite stories. Why are they your favorite?*

2. *What translations of the Bible have your heard about?*

Memorable People

St. Jerome was considered the greatest biblical scholar of his age. (ca. 340 -ca. 420). He devoted himself to biblical studies and an ascetic way of life. For a short time he was the secretary to Pope Damasus, who encouraged him to revise the old Latin Bible. While in Rome he began a scripture study group for women of the upper classes. He was aware that the study of Scripture would change people's live. After the death of Damasus, Jerome traveled to Bethlehem where he completed his translation of the Bible. His translation is called the Vulgate, from the Latin word for "the common people."

Did You Know?

The elements of the ritual described in Nehemiah are found in our Liturgy of the Word: Gathering, Opening Prayer, standing for the proclamation of the Gospel, acclamation of the Word by the assembly, explanation of the Word.

All celebrations of the sacraments include readings from Sacred Scripture. Many communities celebrate Bible Vigils. The study of scripture has greatly increased since Vatican Council II.

The Church Says:

God communicates to us by using words. Just as the hidden, eternal Word of God is made visible to us through the incarnation of Jesus, so too, the message of God is made intelligible to us through our human language.

Catholic reverence for Scripture begins in the belief that there is one single Word communicated by God to us. This one Word is Jesus Christ. The New Testament Scriptures were enthroned at every session of the Second Vatican Council as a "witness" to the proceedings.

We venerate Scripture because these sacred pages were composed through the agency of the Holy Spirit. Its authors were divinely inspired. The books of the Bible teach the truth as God intends it to be revealed, firmly, faithfully and without error. Scripture is to be the foundation of all theological study.

For This Week:

I want to remember:

I want to put my faith into action by:

Questions to Explore

Prayer for the Week

*O God, creator and sustainer of all life,
your word became flesh among us.
We give thanks and praise to You for the gift
of your word.
May your word penetrate our minds,
burn within our hearts
and direct our actions each
and every day of our lives. Amen.*

Scripture:

Jeremiah 1:4-5,17-19
Psalm 71:1-2, 3-4, 5-6, 15, 17
1 Corinthians 12:31–13:13 [or 13:4-13]
Luke 4:21-30

Focus:

OUR IDENTITY AS PROPHETS

Reflection

1. *When have you experienced speaking the truth and feeling rejected by others? Write about this experience.*

2. *List the people or groups of people you find hard to include.*

3. *Reflect on your personal call to be a prophet using the following helps. Write down words, phrases, or peoples names as they surface in your memory.*

   I first knew I was called by God when . . .

   I most often hear God's word in me when . . .

   I find myself . . . afraid, willing, hesitant . . . to speak God's word to others because . . .

   The people who have been prophets in my own life are . . .

Memorable People

Caesar Chavez organized boycotts against the large corporations until better working conditions and wages were achieved for the United Farm Workers.

Dorothy Day began the Catholic Worker movement.

Jean Vanier ministered with the L'Arche community.

Oscar Romero was martyred in working for the rights of the poor in El Salvador.

Did You Know?

February 2 is the feast of the Presentation of the Lord, when Mary and Joseph presented the child Jesus in the temple according to the Jewish law forty days after his birth. It was formerly called Candlemas Day because of the tradition of processing with lighted candles and reciting the famed prayer of Simeon, *Nunc Dimittis* (You can dismiss your servant in peace.) Luke 2:29-32

February 3 is the feast of St. Blaise, bishop and martyr, who is said to have miraculously saved the life of a child choking on a fish-bone. On February 3 it is customary for Catholics to have their throats blessed with a prayer that through the intercession of St. Blaise they be delivered from ailments of the throat and every other evil.

The Church Says:

Prophets hear God's truth within and have the call to speak this truth. Often this truth involves an unpopular message that requires some change in values and behavior. Prophets have long been part of God's workings with the Israelites. The major Hebrew scripture prophets are Isaiah, Jeremiah, Ezekiel, and Daniel. The minor prophets include Amos, Hosea, Micah, and Jonah. Prophets often experienced great difficulty and distress, leading Jeremiah to remark that it would be better if he had not been born. Christ continued to speak a prophetic voice that was not received well in his hometown. As followers of Christ who listen to Gods voice, all Christians are called to speak a prophetic voice. This voice often goes against common values of society and calls for a way of living in harmony with God's ways. The prophetic voice often speaks for just rights for others.

For This Week:

I want to remember:

I want to put my faith into action by:

Questions to Explore

Prayer for the Week

*O God, you have created, formed, and appointed me
to speak your word
of truth and justice for others.
Open my lips.
Put your word in my mouth.
Give me the strength I need to live as Jesus calls me.
Help me stand and walk straight.
Empower me with your love and truth.
I ask this in the name of Jesus. Amen.*

Fifth Sunday in Ordinary Time

Scripture:

Isaiah 6: 1-2a, 3-8
Psalm 138:1-2, 2-3, 4-5, 7-8
1 Corinthians 15:1-11 [or 15:3-8, 11]
Luke 5:1-11

Focus:

TRADITION

Reflection

1. *Describe a time you felt humbled to speak God's word. Who were the people involved, and what was the result of your speaking this word? Write your experience of what it is like to have God work through you in this way.*

2. *Brainstorm the many ways you experience God and list them here. Next to each of these experiences write a word that describes how you feel when you experience God in this way.*

3. *Draw a line across the page signifying your life, and put in five- or 10-year increments from birth to your present age. List all the people who helped you know who God is. Then, using a different color ink, note people with whom you have shared who God is. Write down the primary way you sense God is calling you to reveal who God is to others today.*

Quotable Quotes

"Holy, holy, holy is the LORD of hosts;
the whole earth is full of his glory." Isaiah 6:3

These words from Isaiah are used in the Eucharistic Prayer,

Whom shall I send? Who will go for us? I said: "Here am I, send me!" Isaiah 6:8

Did You Know?

The word revelation literally means unveiling. Through revelation God is unveiled to us.

The Catholic Church uses two creeds: the Apostles Creed, originating in the west and today used in the recitation of the rosary and the Liturgy of the Hours, and the Nicene Creed, from the Council of Nicea used at the Sunday Eucharist since the fifth century.

A person who becomes a pastor takes an Oath of Fidelity to the teaching of the Catholic Church.

The Church Says:

Revelation is the process of God's self-communication in human history. In Biblical times God entered the world of the Israelites through creation, theophanies, dream, prophecy, and historical events. God engages with the community of Israel as well as with individuals. Jesus is the fullest revelation of God. Revelation will be completed with the Second Coming of the Lord. Revelation includes both scripture and tradition. Revelation refers to both the process of what has been communicated, and the content that has been communicated. Revelation is dynamic and continues to unfold. The church clarifies the revelation that is meant for the entire community. God reveals to individuals for their own good as well, but this revelation is not meant for the whole church. Much of the heart of the church's revelation about God is contained in the Nicene Creed. The church hands on this revelation through scripture, liturgy, and sharing her various traditions.

For This Week:

I want to remember:

I want to put my faith into action by:

Questions to Explore

Prayer for the Week

God, you have given the world Jesus Christ
as the fullest expression of who you are.
Help me be continually aware
of all the ways you reveal yourself.
You call and send me
to bring your revelation to others.
May I be an open vessel
to let your voice be spoken through me.
I pray in the name of Jesus. Amen.

Sixth Sunday in Ordinary Time

Scripture:

Jeremiah 17:5-8
Psalm 1:1-2, 3, 4, 6
1 Corinthians 15:12, 16-20
Luke 6:17, 20-26

Focus:

OUR VOCATION TO BEATITUDE

Reflection

Directions: *Think of a time in your life when you have had an experience of being ostracized, insulted, rejected, or misunderstood? Describe the experience. What feelings did you have at the time? How was the experience resolved?*

Questions

1. *Describe what a truly blessed life would be for you.*

2. *How would it be the same and different from your current life?*

3. *What do you need in your life or from this community to live faithfully and trusting in God?*

Quotable Quotes

> St. Augustine describes the fulfillment of the pilgrimage of God's people in his work, the City of God. "There we shall rest and see, we shall see and love, we shall love and praise. Behold what will be at the end without end. For what other end do we have, if not to reach the kingdom which has no end?"
>
> (*De civ. Dei* 22, 30, 5: PL 41, 804)

Did You Know?

Dante Alighieri (1265-1321), an Italian, wrote the *Divine Comedy* which is a poem in three parts (*Inferno, Purgatorio, Paradiso*). Hell is described as an abyss of nine descending circles of various punishments. The poem tells the story of an individual's journey through the circles of hell, up the mount to purgatory, through the spheres of heaven, until the vision of God is attained. Dante draws on various images and metaphors of pilgrimage and journey to finally describe the great crystal rose (another image) in which are situated all of the elect of God, those saved. His descriptions greatly influenced the Christian imagination in the West. Art, poetry, and even theology have drawn on his portrayal of the human quest for beatitude.

In 1880, Auguste Rodin drew upon Dante's *Divine Comedy* in sculpting a work titled "The Gates of Hell."

The Church Says:

The promise of beatitude confronts believers with decisive moral choices and teaches us that true human happiness is not found in worldly wealth, comfort, power, science, and art, however good these realities may be. The Catechism of the Catholic Church teaches us that in God alone, the source of every good thing and of all love, our true human happiness is found. (CCC 1723) Thus the beatific vision is one particular way of describing heaven.

The beatitudes give a foundation for the Church's hope in the fulfillment of God's promise for true happiness. God's desire is that we attain true happiness and goodness in our life and that the attainment of this goal is not just a matter of a strong will on our part. Instead, God, through grace, helps us in our lives to achieve happiness. Ultimately, true joy comes when we enter into full communion with the love of God.

For This Week:

I want to remember:

I want to put my faith into action by:

Questions to Explore

Prayer for the Week

*Loving God, my life is filled with so many good things,
with challenges at work,
with opportunities at home,
with possibilities to learn and grow.*

*I thank you for the gifts I have received
and ask you for the wisdom to manage them.*

*Help me to resist the temptation to pile on
more and more good things
until what I truly love is lost from sight.*

*Give me the courage to throw out the things I do not need,
so that I may in time uncover
my own true self
and my deepest happiness
which is you. Amen.*

from *The Faith Connection* July 13, 1997

Scripture:

1 Samuel 26:2, 7-9, 12-13, 22-23
Psalm 103:1-2, 3-4, 8, 10, 12-13
1 Corinthians 15:45-49
Luke 6:27-38

Focus:

LOVE OF ENEMIES

Reflection

Directions: 1) *Think about some of the unjust ways you have been hurt by others. Now under the column 'Hurts' list ten ways you have been hurt. Use a phrase to describe the circumstances; the person involved and the hurtful event, words, or actions.* 2) *In the next column, "Gifts" list ten ways God uses you: your talents, your best achievements, and your most enjoyable times.* 3) *Times of hurt often begin or deepen our gifts, our appreciation for life, and our gratitude. With a line connect the gifts and hurts that are related.*

HURTS   GIFTS

1.

2.

3.

4.

5.

6.

7.

8.

9.

10.

Questions

1. *What have you learned about loving your enemies from this exercise?*

2. *When a gift arises out of a painful situation, healing is taking place. What areas of hurt and pain still remain to be healed for you?*

3. *What steps can you take to love again?*

Did You Know?

The faith community of *San Egidio* in Rome has a tradition of weekly sung evening prayer after members of the group have assisted the poor in soup kitchens throughout the city. As more and more Italians have joined in this movement, the renown of the community has spread and leaders from both Eastern Europe and North Africa have asked for members of *San Egidio* to establish centers in countries experiencing civil war, to pray for reconciliation between enemies.

The Church Says:

Jesus sacrificed himself for us while we were estranged from God. St. Paul relates to the Romans that Christ died for us sinners while we were yet God's enemies. Thus, Jesus asks of us to live as he himself lived, loving our enemies (CCC 1825).

Simply put, seen from this perspective, the new commandment of Jesus has no fixed boundaries. As disciples of Jesus who follow his teachings, we are to love God and love all. Loving all means to love those close to us, our neighbors, those far off, those we consider "enemies" and loving sinners. Loving without boundaries binds everything together in harmony (CCC 1844).

St. Thomas Aquinas examines the virtue of charity, or love, in his *Summa Theologiae*. Through the practice of love, we participate in the life of the triune God, even though as humans we love imperfectly. Enemies and sinners are loved, for God's sake. (ST 2-2.23.1)

For This Week:

I want to remember:

I want to put my faith into action by:

Questions to Explore

Prayer for the Week

Jesus you loved me enough
to die . . . to surrender all for my salvation.
Open wide the closed fist of my anger
that would rather strike down
those who hurt me
rather than reach out in a clasp of peace.
Open my stingy mind
that would rather remain tied in the
knots of being right
rather than accept the truth and wisdom of letting go.
Open wide my small heart
that would rather wall itself against the
onslaught of my enemies
rather than risk the freedom of loving.
Turn me around to your ways of loving and
fill my hands, mind and heart
with your gracious agape. Amen.

Scripture:

Sirach 27:4-7
Psalm 92:2-3, 13-14, 15-16
1 Corinthians 15:54-58
Luke 6:39-45

Focus:

PRINCIPLES OF CATHOLIC MORALITY

Reflection

Directions: *Read slowly and ponder today's readings.*

Questions

1. *In what ways does your use of the gift of speech build up the kingdom of God? In what ways does your use of the gift of speech tear apart the kingdom of God?*

2. *How is it that we can see the minor faults of our neighbor and miss the major crevasses in our own lives?*

3. *If you were to read your obituary in the paper, what qualities and good deeds would be used to describe your life?*

Did You Know?

A daily examination of conscience is highly recommended. Such a practice can be simply taking a few minutes at the end of each day to review all that happened since morning. Give thanks to God for the good deeds, decisions, and thoughts, ask for forgiveness for anything we might have done that was wrong and forgive anyone who might have offended you in the course of the day.

The great commandment, the ten commandments and the eight beatitudes are also used as a means to examine one's life.

An examination of conscience is completed before celebrating the sacrament of reconciliation.

The Church Says:

Mortal sin must meet three conditions: the object is grave matter, committed with full knowledge, deliberated consent.

Venial sin is defined as either having a less serious matter, or when it does, the sin is committed without full knowledge or complete consent.

Formation of conscience is a life-long project where we prudently sift through our experience and the signs of the times, seek competent advice and with the help of the holy Spirit educate our conscience.

For This Week:

I want to remember:

I want to put my faith into action by:

Questions to Explore

Prayer for the Week

Good and gracious God, take all my liberty.
I give to you my memory, my understanding,
my entire being.
Everything I have and own has been given to me by you,
my God.
To you, I freely return it.
Your will is all that I desire.
Grant me the grace to love you along;
then I am rich and I ask for nothing more. Amen.

(Paraphrase of prayer of St. Ignatius of Loyola,
Founder of the Society of Jesus, the Jesuits)

Ninth Sunday in Ordinary Time

Scripture:

1 Kings 8:41-43
Psalm 117:1-2
Galatians 1:1-2, 6-10
Luke 7:1-10

Focus:

SACRAMENT OF ANOINTING
OF THE SICK

Reflection

1. *Recall a time you felt amazed at the faith of a sick person, or during the illness of a family member. Write about the effect of their faith on you. (Or if you have been ill, write about your experience of faith during your illness.)*

2. *Reflect on the connection between faith and healing. Jesus said that in one town he could not work any miracles (including healing) because of a lack of faith. Yet, if one has faith healing does not always occur. Describe your beliefs about faith and healing.*

3. *When Jesus healed people he often said, Your sins are forgiven. Write about your understanding of the connection between spiritual and physical healing. List some of the ways the church community is able to participate in the healing process of others.*

Quotable Quotes

"Are any among you sick? . . . have them pray over them,
anointing them with oil in the Name of the Lord." James 5:14

"Through this holy anointing, may the Lord in his love and mercy help you with
the grace of the Holy Spirit. Amen. May the Lord who frees you
from sin save you and raise you up. Amen." (Rite of Anointing and Pastoral Care of the Sick, n. 25.)

Memorable People

Mother Teresa cares for the sick who are the poorest of the poor in India.

Father Damien ministers to the physical and spiritual needs of 600 lepers on the Hawaiian Island of Molokai until he became helpless after catching the disease himself.

St. Dymphna, from the town of Geel in Belgium, is the patroness of those with mental illnesses.

Sister Anthony O'Connell, S.C., brought nursing to the Civil War battlefield.

Dr. Tom Dooley is well known for his medical work in Asia.

Did You Know?

The preferred way of celebrating the Sacrament of the Sick is with family or the larger community present.

For a long period of time in the Church's history, the anointing of the sick was done by the laity.

The prayer said before communion: "Lord, I am not worthy that you should come under my roof. Speak but the word and my soul shall be healed" comes from Luke 7:6-7

The Church Says:

In his healing ministry of the sick and in the forgiveness of sin Christ looked for the presence of faith. Physical illness is not the result of sin or a punishment from God. A time of sickness may be an occasion for a person to draw closer to God. The church reaches out to those who are sick in various ways: visitations, various family needs and supports, networks of prayer, and the Sacrament of the Sick. The Sacrament of the Anointing of the Sick finds its origin in the healing ministry of Christ, an at one time was called Extreme Unction. Extreme Unction was limited to an anointing just before the time of death. Today the church celebrates the Sacrament of the Anointing of the Sick at times of illness and for the elderly, often in the presence of the family or even at a parish Mass. A person who has already died is not anointed. Other prayers are prayed are for them.

For This Week:

I want to remember:

I want to put my faith into action by:

Questions to Explore

Prayer for the Week

As the centurion, I pray in faith
  asking that you bring healing
  to my sisters and brothers, (N) . . .
Let them know of your presence and care.
I trust that you desire
  wholeness and happiness for them.
Bring them strength in spirit and body.
I pray through Christ,
  the healer and Savior of all. Amen.

Scripture:

1 Kings 17:17-24
Psalm 30:2, 4, 5-6, 11, 12, 13
Galatians 1:11-19
Luke 7:11-17

Focus:

RESURRECTION OF THE BODY

Reflection

1. *Recall a time you felt dead. Note your feelings and actions at that time. Describe how God brought you back to life.*

2. *Imagine the end of the world with all who have lived. Picture the scene of everyone, including all people you have known, raised to new life. Picture yourself, too. Jot down words to describe what you see.*

3. *Breathe and sense your body as a temple of the Holy Spirit. List some ways you care for your body, this temple of the Holy Spirit. List some ways you neglect your body.*

Quotable Quotes

"Go and tell John what you have seen and heard, the blind receive their sight, the lame walk, the lepers are cleansed, the deaf hear, the dead are raised, the poor have good news brought to them." Luke 7:22

"Do you not know that you are God's temple, and that God's Spirit dwells in you? . . . God's temple is holy, and you are that temple." 1 Corinthians 3:16-17

Did You Know?

Ezekiel 37 portrays a powerful and well-known image of God pulling together strewn dry bones and breathing new life into them. The dry bones are an image of God's people.

The Church holds the body of the deceased person sacred, incenses it at the Mass of Christian burial, and believes it is awaiting the resurrection of the body.

Early Christians marked graves with the initials RIP (Latin for rest in peace), denoting their belief in the resurrection of the body. The grave was a place of resting or sleeping in peace until the time when Christ would call forth those who had died believing in him.

The Church Says:

Beginning with Adam, God breathes life into the human person. People are whole, body and spirit. Both are necessary for the wholeness of the person. At the time of physical death, the body dies. At the end of time, God will raise our bodies and reunite our spirits with them. This resurrected body will never die again. The Creed states the belief in the resurrection of the body. Elijah prayed God would raise the widows son, and Christ raised the son of the widow of Naim, as well as Lazarus. They will die again. Christ is the first to have a resurrected body that will never die again. Scripture accounts of the resurrection appearances give some glimpses of what the risen body is like.

For This Week:

I want to remember:

I want to put my faith into action by:

Questions to Explore

Prayer for the Week

Sitting in God's presence,

breathe God's breath in and out without words.

Simply be present to God

through your body's breath.

When your mind wanders,

return to feeling your breath come in

and go out of your body.

Sit in this prayer of quiet

for five or ten minutes.

Then reflect on your experience.

Eleventh Sunday in Ordinary Time

Scripture:

2 Samuel 12:7-10, 13
Psalm 32:1-2, 5, 7, 11
Galatians 2:16, 19-21
Luke 7:36-8:3 [or 7:36-50]

Focus:

SACRAMENT OF RECONCILIATION

Reflection

Directions: *Think of a time in your life when you needed to ask someone for their forgiveness. Describe the situation and the emotions you felt. Then describe how you felt once you were reconciled.*

Questions

1. *What is it that gets in our way when we need to admit that we have done wrong?*

2. *Why is it so difficult to ask for forgiveness?*

Did You Know?

Catholics relate all sorts of stories of pre-Vatican II experiences in the confessional box. Still, more rigorous was the practice of penance in the early Church, when the process of reconciliation for sinners who committed grave sin (idolatry, murder, adultery) entailed a public discipline and could last for years. this practice was known as the Order of Penitents. In the seventh century, Irish missionaries introduced to Continental Europe the practice of "private" penance, which did not require such prolonged and public completion of penitential practices as experienced in the Order of Penitents. From then on, the sacramental practice has been performed privately between priest and penitent. The Second Vatican Council, in its reform of sacraments, emphasized their communal nature. One form of the celebration of Reconciliation places it within a Liturgy of the Word which includes an examination of conscience and the praise of God's mercy. But the actual confessing of sins follows privately.

The Church Says:

Because of the various realities involved in this sacrament, it goes by various names. In addition to being called the sacrament of Reconciliation, it is also called the sacrament of conversion, the sacrament of penance, the sacrament of confession, and the sacrament of forgiveness. This variety of names suggests the significance and complexity of the mystery which is expressed and experienced by this sacrament which continues the healing ministry of Jesus.

The official formula used by the priest in the sacrament to express the healing which takes place in Reconciliation emphasizes what we believe: God alone reconciles us to himself through Jesus Christ, and the Church carries on this ministry which effects pardon and peace to those who so desperately need and desire it.

For This Week:

I want to remember:

I want to put my faith into action by:

Questions to Explore

Prayer for the Week

An Act of Contrition
My God,
I am sorry for my sins with all my heart.
In choosing to do wrong
and failing to do good,
I have sinned against you
whom I should love above all things.
I firmly intend, with your help,
to do penance,
to sin no more,
and to avoid whatever leads me to sin.
Our Savior Jesus Christ
suffered and died for us.
In his name, my God, have mercy.

Rite for Reconciliation of Individual Penitents

Twelfth Sunday in Ordinary Time

Scripture:

Zechariah 12:10-11; 13:1
Psalm 63:2, 3-4, 5-6, 8-9
Galatians 3:26-29
Luke 9:18-24

Focus:

THE CROSS IN THE LIFE OF THE CHRISTIAN

Reflection

Directions: *Take some time to recall your own life, especially those times when suffering, carrying the cross, seemed to prevail. Write your own story of taking up the cross of suffering, using phrases and images to outline the circumstances and outcomes.*

Questions

1. *How has my suffering led me to deeper faith?*

2. *How would I describe the victory of the cross in my life?*

3. *How do I find consolation in knowing that my suffering is united with Jesus' passion and death?*

4. *What new attitudes can I foster regarding the daily struggles and pain of my life?*

Did You Know?

Our baptism into the cross of Jesus figures prominently in Catholic liturgical practice and devotion. Upon entering and leaving church, Catholics sign themselves the sign of the cross using holy water. At the start of every Mass, we sign ourselves. At the Rite of Acceptance, the sign of the cross is marked upon catechumens. At the beginning of the Rite of Infant Baptism, the baby is signed with the cross by parents and godparents. At the Rite of Reception of the Bishop in the Cathedral Church, the ordinary kisses the cross at the doors of the church. In all of these gestures, we acknowledge the primacy of this symbol and our acceptance of the "gospel of suffering."

The Church Says:

This holy cross of Jesus, which is at once a horror and an honor, enables John Paul II to create a new term, the gospel of suffering. He movingly writes about Jesus who transforms our suffering, and in that transformation points that hurting person to a place close to the Lord himself. "It is He—as the interior Master and Guide—who reveals to the suffering brother and sister this wonderful interchange, situated at the very heart of the mystery of Redemption. Suffering is, in itself, an experience of evil. But Christ has made suffering the firmest basis of the definitive good. By His suffering on the cross, Christ reached the very roots of evil, of sin and death. He conquered the author of evil, Satan, and his permanent rebellion against the Creator. To the suffering brother and sister, Christ discloses and gradually reveals the horizons of the kingdom of God: the horizons of a world converted to the Creator, of a world free from sin, a world being built on the saving power of love." (SD 26) Through the very heart of the experience of suffering, we know that we are led into the kingdom of God, for suffering cannot be transformed and changed from the outside, but only from within the very depths of a person through the Spirit. Thus, we believe that the way in which followers of Jesus pick up their cross and follow the Master is a matter of the heart, the interior spirit and love.

For This Week:

I want to remember:

I want to put my faith into action by:

Questions to Explore

Prayer for the Week

St. John of the Cross, Stanzas of the Soul

O, living flame of love That tenderly wounded my soul in its deepest center, Since thou are no longer oppressive, perfect me now if it be thy will, Break the web of this sweet encounter.

Oh, sweet burn! Oh, delectable wound! Oh, soft hand! Oh, delicate touch that savours of eternal life and pays every debt! In slaying, thou hast changed death into life.

Oh, lamps of fire, in whose splendours the deep caverns of sense which were dark and blind with strange brightness. Give heat and light together to their Beloved!

How gently and lovingly thou awakenest in my bosom where thou dwellest secretly and alone! And in they sweet breathing, full of blessing and glory, how delicately thou inspirest my love![1]

[1] Peers, E. Allison (ed) *St. John of the Cross: Living Flame of Love*, Garden City, NY: Image Books, 1962, p. 30.

Thirteenth Sunday in Ordinary Time

Scripture:

1 Kings 19:16b, 19-21
Psalm 16:1-2, 5, 7-8, 9-10, 11
Galatians 5:1, 13-18
Luke 9:51-62

Focus:

CHRISTIAN FREEDOM

Reflection

Directions: *Read slowly and ponder the readings for this Sunday.*

Questions

1. *What do understand to be the vocation of every Christian?*

2. *In what ways have you freely responded to God's invitation for you to follow Christ? How does what you do fulfill God's will?*

3. *Describe your struggles to keep Christ as the center of your life.*

Quotable Quotes

"We belong to God and to one another;
this is our deepest identity and our noblest vocation."

Pope John XXIII

Did You Know?

The Spiritual Exercises of St. Ignatius Loyola (d. 1556) aim at increasing the freedom of the one who makes them. They stress a freedom from inordinate attachments and choosing to follow the way of Christ in all our decisions and actions.

The Church Says:

God calls us to serve the divine plan in spirit and truth. We are bound to God in conscience but not coerced. Humans must be guided by their own judgments and enjoy the freedom to do so. This truth is manifested most fully in Jesus Christ.

The freedom given to us by God does not mean we can do whatever it is that we want. The Second Vatican Council noted that in modern times people prize freedom and eagerly strive for it. But it is often cherished improperly, as if it gives total autonomy and license to an individual, to the point of doing evil.

Catholic moral theology holds that freedom is not authentic unless it is in the service of what is good and just. Choosing to do otherwise, to disobey and do evil, abuses the freedom we have in Christ. Freedom means that we are free to act responsibly.

For This Week:

I want to remember:

I want to put my faith into action by:

Questions to Explore

Prayer for the Week

God, all faith is a gift from you.
As I continue on this journey of faith,
*   help my faith to deepen each and every day.*
I desire to understand and love you
*   more and more each day.*
Take away the doubts that cause me to hesitate
*   on this journey or turn away from you.*
I rely on your promise to never forget me,
*   and the reminder that you have carved me*
*   in the palm of your hand.*

Scripture:

Isaiah 66:10-14c
Psalm 66:1-3, 4-5, 6-7, 16, 20
Galatians 6:14-18
Luke 10:1-12, 17-20 [or 10:1-9]

Focus:

THE CHURCH EXISTS IN ORDER TO EVANGELIZE

Reflection

Directions: *Think about a message of God's love you have heard in your own life. Describe or explain. How are you discovering you want to share this good news with others?*

Questions

1. *What are some obstacles and resistance to hearing and receiving the good news?*

2. *What gifts do you have to offer in bringing the good news to others?*

Did You Know?

The patron saints of foreign missions are St. Francis Xavier and Therese of Lisieux.

Japanese novelist Shusako Endo has written a variety of novels. Two of them deal with the early evangelization efforts in Japan. *The Samurai* grapples with failure of initial missionary efforts in the sixteenth century. *Silence* (1976) is about the Japanese Catholic martyrs. It is of this latter work that Graham Greene writes, "In my opinion one of the finest novels of our time."

The Church Says:

Born through the evangelization efforts of Jesus, the Church, in turn, engages in self-evangelization and the evangelization of the world. The purpose of both this external and internal evangelization is conversion, to make of all the world and everyone in it that "new creation" (Revelation 21:5). For, if the gospel is proclaimed and accepted, then humanity's judgment, determining values, points of interest, lines of thought, sources of inspiration, and models of life which are contrary to the good news will be upset and reformed. (EN 19) In other words, what is being evangelized is culture, not superficially, but radically and vitally, to its depth.

For This Week:

I want to remember:

I want to put my faith into action by:

Questions to Explore

Prayer for the Week

Almighty God,
all the earth rejoices and cries out to you with joy.
You save your people and set them free.
You fulfill your promises
and we proclaim your good news to all the world.
Guide our feet in your ways,
inspire our hearts and minds
to give witness to your love,
fill us with your courage
to proclaim the good news of your Son, Jesus Christ.

Fifteenth Sunday in Ordinary Time

Scripture:

Deuteronomy 30:10-14
Psalm 69:14, 17, 30-31, 33-34, 36, 37
Colossians 1:15-20
Luke 10:25-37

Focus:

LOVE OF NEIGHBOR

Reflection

Directions: *Take time to think about these Works of Mercy as they are operative in your life. After each action jot down a specific example of how you have internalized these actions of loving your neighbor.*

CORPORAL WORKS OF MERCY	SPIRITUAL WORKS OF MERCY
Feed the hungry	*Admonish the sinner*
Give drink to the thirsty	*Instruct the ignorant*
Clothe the naked	*Counsel the doubtful*
Visit the imprisoned	*Comfort the sorrowful*
Shelter the homeless	*Bear wrongs patiently*
Visit the sick and bury the dead	*Forgive all injuries*
	Pray for the living and the dead

Questions

1. *What actions for loving your neighbor do you need to further incorporate into your life?*

2. *How can you expand the works of mercy to include the stranger, the unlikable and those with whom you have differences?*

Quotable Quotes

"If I cannot find the face of Jesus in the face of those who are my enemies, if I cannot find him in the unbeautiful, if I cannot find him in those who have the 'wrong ideas,' if I cannot find him in the poor and the defeated, then I will not find him in the bread or the wine.

"If I do not reach out in this world to those with whom he has identified himself, why do I imagine that I want to be with him, and them, in heaven? Why do I think I want to be for all eternity in the company of those whose companionship I avoided every day of my life." Peter Maurin (partner with Dorothy Day)

Did You Know?

Our Catholic understanding is that these spiritual and corporal works of mercy are prime actions that help us realize the love of neighbor which Jesus enjoined upon his followers. These actions, when rendered to another believer, help build up the body of Christ, and when show to non-believers help to evangelize them.

The Church Says:

The Second Vatican Council teaches, "works of charity have become much more urgent and worldwide, now that means of communication are more rapid, distance between [people] has been more or less conquered, people in every part of the globe have become as members of a single family. Charitable actions today can and should reach all [people] and all needs. Whenever [people] are to be found who are in want of food and drink, of clothing, housing, medicine, work, education, the means necessary for leading a truly human life, wherever there are [people] racked with misfortune or illness, [those] suffering exile or imprisonment, Christian charity should go in search of them and find them out, comfort them with devoted care and give them the helps that will relieve their needs." (*Apostolicam Actuositatem*, 18 November 1965, n. 8)

For This Week:

I want to remember:

I want to put my faith into action by:

Questions to Explore

Prayer for the Week

Dorothy Day [1]

Merciful Creator of us all,
in Christ Jesus, your Son, our Risen Saviour,
you have brought light to the blind,
comfort to the afflicted.
and good news to the poor.

We now remember with heartfelt thanksgiving
the generosity of spirit
manifest in the life and labors
of your devoted servant, Dorothy Day.

In times of unrelieved hardship
*   and economic depression*
as well as in widespread prosperity
*   and abundance*
she spent herself in dedicated partnership
with the privations and disdain
felt by the homeless and the unwanted
as a champion of their rights.

An early, often, lonely witness
in the cause of peace and conscience,
at once fearless and gentle,
she braved the disapproval of the powerful,
rejection by the many who did not
*   understand,*
and even imprisonment.

Grant that we in turn may be moved
by your Holy Spirit, Father,
to share her compassion and concern
as true disciples of the Lord Jesus,
giving ourselves as she did
to the love and care
of the neediest members of Christ's Body
and committing our lives, our means,
even our homes,
to bring the light and hope,
the justice and peace of the gospel
to all your people.
This we pray in the Holy Spirit
through Jesus Christ, our Lord. Amen.

[1] Prayer card available from Salt, 205 W. Monroe St., Chicago, IL 60606.

Sixteenth Sunday in Ordinary Time

Scripture:

Genesis 18:1-10a
Psalm 15:2-3, 3-4, 5
Colossians 1:24-28
Luke 10:38-42

Focus:

TO BE HEARERS OF THE WORD

Reflection

Directions: *Read slowly and ponder the readings for this Sunday.*

Questions

1. *Name all the ways you receive messages in this age of communication. What criteria do you need in order to prioritize the importance of the messages received? What importance do you place on personally delivered messages?*

2. *How do hear the Word of God and its message? How do you respond to its message? When do you find it difficult to follow? Why?*

Quotable Quotes

"In accord with the teachings of the Second Vatican Council, all will thus regard sacred Scripture as the abiding source of spiritual life, the foundation for Christian instruction, and the core of all theological study." Apostolic Constitution of Paul VI 3 April 1969

Did You Know?

Scripture is to be the foundation of all theological study.

The Bible is always to be treated with reverence. It is the Word of God. Bible is called by many names: The Holy Book, The Holy Bible, Scriptures, The Word of God, The Word.

The Lectionary is name of the book used at Mass which contains the Scripture readings.

The Church Says:

The Word of God is not a dry word limited to the printed page or to the spoken proclamation. It is a living Word whose intimated truth is revealed in Jesus Christ through his life, his ministry, his suffering, death and resurrection. The apostles and their successors witness to the truth revealed in the person of Jesus Christ, the incarnate Word of God.

In Scripture we have the truth about Jesus and his message for us. The evangelists composed their record based on oral tradition and in the light of the situation in their own communities of faith.

The Second Vatican Council document, *Dei Verbum*, states: "It follow that all the preaching of the Church, as indeed the entire Christian religion, should be nourished and ruled by Sacred Scripture. In the sacred books the Father who is in heaven comes lovingly to meet his children, and talks with them." (DV, 18)

For This Week:

I want to remember:

I want to put my faith into action by:

Questions to Explore

Prayer for the Week

*O God, you have given us our senses that we might
hear, see, touch, feel and smell
the wonders of creation.
Bless us so that we might use these senses to better hear
your Word in order to put it into practice
in our daily lives.
Help us to bring the Good News of Jesus Christ to those
who have been pushed aside by society.
May we, like Martha and Mary, become both hearers
and doers of the Gospel message.
We ask this through Jesus Christ, our brother,
who lives and reigns with you and the Holy Spirit,
one God forever and ever. Amen.*

Seventeenth Sunday in Ordinary Time

Scripture:

Genesis 18:20-32
Psalm 138:1-2, 2-3, 6-7, 7-8
Colossians 2:12-14
Luke 11:1-13

Focus:

THE LORD'S PRAYER:
SUMMARY OF THE GOSPEL.

Reflection

1. *Imagine yourself being held in God's arms as a child being held by a loving parent. What do you like or dislike about this image? Write how you picture or sense God when you bring a need to prayer.*

2. *Dependence on God is easier for some people than others. List things for which you depend on God. Then list ways you try to control your life yourself. After that, describe the ways have you been letting God be more in control of your life.*

3. *Some parts of the Lord's Prayer are easy to pray, and some parts challenge us. Write about the part of the Lord's Prayer you find most meaningful for you now.*

Quotable Quotes

"(The Lord) answered,
For the sake of ten I will not destroy it
(the city of Sodom and Gomorrah)."
Genesis 18:32

Memorable People

St. Ignatius Loyola's feast is July 31. Ignatius, founder of the worldwide Society of Jesus (Jesuits), is well known for his Spiritual Exercises and rules for discernment. He himself had a profound conversion experience when recovering from a battle wound and having nothing to read but the bible. Ignatius died in Rome on July 31, 1556.

St. Alphonsus Liguori's feast is August 1. Alphonsus was a bishop and founder of the Congregation of the Most Holy Redeemer, commonly called Redemptorists, at Scala, Italy, in 1732 for mission work among the poor in Europe.

Did You Know?

In the gospels Jesus uses the term Abba to address God. This is a very familiar form which indicates the close, trusting relationship of a child with a parent.

The Lord's Prayer is stated differently by Matthew and Luke.

The Lord's Prayer, even when prayed alone, is always a communal prayer.

The Church Says:

The Our Father sums up the entire Gospel. This prayer is not just a collection of prayers. Jesus, the Word of God, gave us this prayer. Jesus teaches us to address God as he does in the very personal sense of "Father." "Abba" is more precisely translated "Daddy," and expresses the trust and dependence of a child in calling a parent "Daddy" or "Mommy." We are able to address God in this way because we are adopted sons and daughters through the Holy Spirit. In the Our Father the needs we pray for bring us more fully into communion with God and the ways of Gods kingdom. The Our Father, even when prayed alone by an individual, is communal and is a prayer for the entire Church.

For This Week:

I want to remember:

I want to put my faith into action by:

Questions to Explore

Prayer for the Week

Lord God, out of his own prayer,
Jesus taught his disciples to pray
the Lord's Prayer.
Teach me to pray this prayer
not only in words
but in the depth of my being.
Open me to greater trust in you.
Help me depend more on you
and less on myself.
I pray this in the name of Jesus. Amen.

Scripture:

Ecclesiastes 1:2; 2:21-23
Psalm 90:3–4, 5–6, 12–13, 14, 17
Colossians 3:1-5,9-11
Luke 12:13-21

Focus:

THE TENTH COMMANDMENT AND THE SEVEN DEADLY SINS

Reflection

1. *How have you experienced greed trying to gain a hold on you? What choices have you made to go along with greed? What choices have you made against the pull of greed?*

2. *What does it mean to grow rich before God? How is God inviting you to take a next step in growing rich in God's ways?*

3. *We all need the support of others to choose God's ways. The church offers this support through its people, its prayer and worship, and through its spirituality. List the ways has the church already supported you to make choices that go against the pulls of the various capital sins. Then list other ways you see the church offering you support in which you may engage in the future.*

Quotable Quotes

"Vanity of vanities! All is vanity!" Ecclesiastes 1:2

Jesus said, "Be on your guard against all kinds of greed." Luke 12:15

Memorable People

St. Francis of Assisi is legendary for his gesture of revoking possessions in stripping naked and walking in the street away from them.

St. John Mary Vianney, commonly called the Cure D'Ars, studied for the priesthood for many years because he had great difficulty with the Latin language. He was finally ordained in 1815. He is the patron of parish priests, especially confessors because in the latter part of his life he spent from 16 to 18 hours a day in the confessional to be available to people who came from all over to seek his counsel. His feast day is August 4.

Did You Know?

In most religious communities men and women take the vow of poverty as a way of living out the gospel value of detachment from greed. The vow allows these women and men to use various goods, but ownership of cars and other items is retained by the religious community itself.

The Church Says:

Christ instructed his followers to avoid greed in all its forms. This directive is also found in the tenth commandment. The church promotes the positive use of possessions, but states that greed, the inordinate attachment to possessions is one of the capital or deadly sins. All of the seven deadly sins, i.e., pride, greed, envy, wrath, lust, gluttony, and sloth gradually pull a person in a direction away from God. Societal values often encourage these sins. The gospel invites people to continually open their hearts to be directed by the everlasting values of God's kingdom. The church provides support to turn from sin and to live in freedom as God's sons and daughters in Christ.

For This Week:

I want to remember:

I want to put my faith into action by:

Questions to Explore

Prayer for the Week

God, you are the source of my life.

I belong to you.

You give my life meaning.

You invite me to live my life by values

that will bring true and lasting happiness.

Fill my heart with desire for you and the gifts you offer.

I ask this through Christ, the Lord. Amen.

Nineteenth Sunday in Ordinary Time

Scripture:

Wisdom 18:6-9
Psalm 33:1, 12, 18-19, 20-22
Hebrews 11:1-2, 8-19 [or 11:1-2, 8-12]
Luke 12:32-48 [or 12:35-40]

Focus:

CHRISTIAN HOPE

Reflection

The doctors spoke in soft tones, to the husband of 28 years, as his wife lay in a coma in the trauma room. The accident left him with a mere broken leg, but her body was badly crushed against the frame of the automobile and her brain was damaged. "While we saved her life, under impossible odds," they said, "if she does come out of this coma, she will be a vegetable." The husband shook his head stubbornly and fled to the quiet of the hospital chapel. There he prayed as never before. Through his tears and pleadings, a great sense of peace surrounded him as he surrendered everything to God. He was overwhelmed with the conviction that she would recover and placed his entire hope on the God of peace who seemed near enough to touch. As the weeks wore on, little signs of her recovery were perceptible. Each day, he faithfully prayed by her side. He never missed a day, letting his business and all those things, which had preoccupied his life, go. Her struggle to regain and maintain consciousness was visible to all who came to pray as was his faithful trust in God's power to heal. Gradually she recovered, learning to walk, talk and read all over again. Within six months, and after several operations to mend her crushed bones, she was fully recovered. His hope in the God who heals took the couple through many struggles, during and since that recovery. For them, hope perpetuates itself, through the remembering of that moment of peace in the hospital chapel.

Questions

Write your own story of hope in the space below:

The Church Says:

The *Catechism* speaks of "hope" in two places, as a theological virtue and in its exposition on the first commandment. To understand this key concept, let us first explore the theological virtues. These are distinguished from human virtue in that faith, hope and love are gifts instilled by God and orient us toward union with the Trinity. They are, if you will, the highest of virtues. Faith, hope and love are the firm foundation of the correct moral life precisely because they have their origin in the Triune God (CCC 1812-13). While they are given to us by God, they can, however, be perfected in the exercise of our Christian life or squandered by our neglect.

Christian hope is centered in the person of Jesus, his preaching, especially the beatitudes as they outline for us the path that takes us through difficulties in this life to the life that awaits us on high. Hope is also a weapon in the war against evil, our breastplate (see 1 Thessalonians 5:8). Hope is nourished and sustained in prayer, especially the prayer that Jesus taught us wherein we express our longing for the coming kingdom, here yet not fully (CCC 1820).

For This Week:

I want to remember:

I want to put my faith into action by:

Questions to Explore

Prayer for the Week

Loving God, You promise the richness
and treasure of that heavenly mansion
that you are already preparing for me.
Jesus, You have spoken many times of this hope
for a heavenly place, of which I could not even dream.
But, is my hope just for a future, distant heaven
where my hopes and needs will be met?
Will you not offer me a bit of heaven on earth?
just a glimpse of that beauty?
just a moment of sweet peace?
just a short respite from the burdens I carry?
Yes, you are a God of the here and now.
You have not abandoned me or
left me to fend for myself.
You are my hope in all the struggles and failures of my life.
You ask that I wait and watch as you
weave your hope throughout the tapestry of my life.

Twentieth Sunday in Ordinary Time

Scripture:

Jeremiah 38:4-6, 8-10
Psalm 40:2, 3, 4, 18
Hebrews 12:1-4
Luke 12:49-53

Focus:

CONFLICT BETWEEN GOOD AND EVIL

Reflection

Directions: *Reflect, thoughtfully, upon this difficult reading, then respond to the questions.*

I have come to set the earth on fire, and how I wish it were already blazing! There is a baptism with which must be baptized, and how great is my anguish until it is accomplished! Do you think that I have come to establish peace on the earth? No, I tell you, but rather division. From now on a household of five will be divided, three against two and two against three; a father will be divided against his son and a son against his father, a mother against her daughter and a daughter against her mother, a mother-in-law against her daughter-in-law and a daughter-in-law against her mother-in-law. (Luke 12:49-53)

Questions

1. *When did a choice made by Jesus, cause him suffering? Be specific.*

2. *When were you faced with a difficult choice, the consequences of which would cause division in your family or circle of friends?*

3. *How has pain or suffering in your life purified or cleansed you?*

Quotable Quotes

"There are two ways, one of life and one of death:
and great is the difference between the two ways. The way of life is this:
first, you shall love God, who created you; second, your neighbor as yourself." (*Didache* 1:1)

Did You Know?

In the Babylonian creation myth, the *Enuma Elish*, two gods battle, the good god, Marduk, and the evil monster-god, Tiamat. Marduk wins and in winning chaos is controlled and good triumphs and the cosmic order that had been threatened is restored. In the Genesis creation account it is clear that God alone creates and is solely responsible for all goodness. There was no battle between a good god and an evil god or force.

The Church Says:

The Catholic theology of creation has its foundation in this understanding and has three basic points. The first is that we have affirmed from the earliest times that God created ex nihilo or, "out of nothing." This means that there was not some sort of pre-existent material, but that everything in creation owes its existence to God. Even though there is evil in the world, someday God will overcome it. The second point is that God created the world good. This is a refrain echoed in the Genesis account (1:1-2:4) and that therefore evil is not the result of God. Through our human freedom, somehow evil entered the world after God created it. The third point is that since creation is the handiwork of God, we humans can come to know God through it by the efforts of our reason (although the fullness of revelation is found in Jesus Christ).

Thus, Scripture and Catholic theology attests that good and evil are not equal principles, with equal force. God is more powerful than evil. We know that in Christ, God triumphs over evil. And yet, evil does exist.

For This Week:

I want to remember:

I want to put my faith into action by:

Questions to Explore

Prayer for the Week

Where are you God,
when children of this world are
starving and abused and murdered?
Where are you God,
amidst the wars, street fights, and
violence that pervades this planet
and bombards my senses on the nightly news?
Where are you God
when deadly cancer, AIDS,
and heart attack strike
my family and friends?
You are here, in this present moment
of pain, suffering, and death.
You stand with me in the midst
of evil, violence, and killing.
You are full of goodness, life and truth,
edging me on to take up your Way,
moving me to act in your Truth,
empowering me to give your Life.

Twenty-first Sunday in Ordinary Time

Scripture:

Isaiah 66:18-21
Psalm 117:1, 2
Hebrews 12:5-7, 11-13
Luke 13:22-30

Focus:

FINAL JUDGMENT

Reflection

Directions: *Read Isaiah 66:18-21 and Luke 13: 22-30.*

Questions

1. *Who would you include in heaven?*

2. *Name who is included in the House of the Lord.*

3. *What do you think is meant by "the narrow door"?*

Did You Know?

Michelangelo's fresco of the "Last Judgment" is on the back wall of the Sistine Chapel in the Vatican. The Sistine Chapel is where the election of the new Pope is held.

Catholics believe that the people who lived before the birth of Christ were taken up into heaven at the time of Jesus' resurrection.

The Church Says:

There are two moments of judgment. At one's death, God judges the moral quality of one's total life, how one has chosen fundamentally to either cooperate with God's grace or how one has chosen to reject God's grace. Accordingly, judgment is rendered and the person is assigned to either heaven, purgatory or hell. This immediate judging after one's death is called the particular judgment.

The final or last judgment also constitutes God's final word on all of history. Jesus Christ, who is the living Word of God, will reveal God's glorious triumph over evil and at the same time manifest the ultimate meaning of the whole word of creation. Then, all will be revealed concerning the way divine providence has led everything to this completion. At the Last Judgment, there is only heaven and hell for all of eternity.

The meaning of the last judgment for believers is an urgent call to conversion, to make the best use of the time available. The Church, in this regard, speaks of holy fear, that feeling which commits us to the justice of God's kingdom and pursuing the way of life in Christ rather than the way of death.

For This Week:

I want to remember:

I want to put my faith into action by:

Questions to Explore

Prayer for the Week

Most loving God, you desire that all people
will be one with you in heaven for all eternity.
Help each of us to live each day according to your desire.
When we forget what your desire is,
send a gentle reminder that heaven is for all eternity.
Grant that when each of us comes to the end of
our earthly life, you will find us
ready to meet you face to face.
Bless us with perseverance, acceptance, and patience
each and every day of our lives.

Twenty-second Sunday in Ordinary Time

Scripture:

Sirach 3:17-18, 20, 28-29
Psalm 68:4-5, 6-7, 10-11
Hebrews 12:18-19, 22-24a
Luke 14:1, 7-14

Focus:

PREFERENTIAL OPTION FOR THE POOR

Reflection

Directions: Recall an experience with an individual or situation involving the poor. Describe the experience. What impact did it have on you?

Questions

1. *How can the deprivation of the poor hurt us all?*

2. *What are some implications for you personally in light of the gospel message of the preferential option for the poor?*

Quotable Quotes

St. Rose of Lima (1586-1617) is the first canonized saint of the Americas. She is the patron saint of South America and the Philippines. Her reputation was that of a mystic with extraordinary gifts, who took as her model St. Catherine of Siena, living a reclusive life and practicing extreme mortification and penance. Early on, however, when her mother chided her for caring for the poor and sick at home, St. Rose of Lima responded, "When we serve the poor and the sick, we serve Jesus. We must not fail to help our neighbors, because in them we serve Jesus." (P. Hansen, *Vita mirabilis*, Louvain, 1668)

Did You Know?

St. Anthony of Padua (1191-1231) was a Franciscan friar and renowned preacher who was accorded the title "Doctor of the Church." An Italian, he began as a missionary to North Africa but returned home due to illness. Back in Italy, his renown grew as a preacher and scholar and he eventually was given permission by Francis to teach theology to the friars. For a time, he pursued this teaching mission in southern France. His sermons are marked by a concern for social problems. This concern is reflected in the practice today of St. Anthony's Bread, contributions from which assist the relief of the poor.

The Church Says:

In our Catholic teaching, the purpose of society is to ensure a proper framework to promote the conditions for both associations and individuals to obtain what is their due, given their nature and vocation. Social justice relies, therefore, on the notion of the "common good," defined as the "sum total of social conditions which allow people, either as groups or as individuals, to reach their fulfillment more fully and easily." (GS, 26) Thus, the common good concerns all. And, that concern focuses on making accessible to each those basic things that provide a genuine human life: food, clothing, housing, health, work, education, culture, suitable information, the right to establish a family, privacy, and so on. (CCC 1908)

It is within this context of the Catholic social teaching and our understanding of the common good, combined with the Church's reflection on the good news of Jesus Christ that a preferential option for the poor has been articulated. We believe that God blesses those who help the poor and there is a definite gospel imperative for us to act for when the "poor have the good news preached to them" it is a sign of the presence of Christ (Mt 11:5; Lk 4:8). A love for the poor has been a constant hallmark of the Church's tradition. As one of the fathers of the Church has vigorously insisted, "Not to enable the poor to share in our goods is to steal from them and deprive them of life. The goods we possess are not ours, but theirs." (St. John Chrysostom, *Homiliae in Lazarum* 2,5: PG 48, 992D)

For This Week:

I want to remember:

I want to put my faith into action by:

Questions to Explore

Prayer for the Week

Open our eyes to the needs of all;
inspire us with words and deeds
to comfort those who labor and are burdened;
keep our service of others faithful
to the example and command of Christ.

Let your church be a living witness
to truth and freedom,
to justice and peace,
that all people may be lifted up
by the hope of a world made new.

(Roman Missal, Eucharistic Prayer for Masses for Various Needs and Occasions IV: Jesus, the Compassion of God)

Scripture:

Wisdom 9:13-18b
Psalm 90:3-4, 5-6, 12-13, 14-17
Philemon 9-10, 12-17
Luke 14:25-33

Focus:

**THE JOURNEY OF THE DISCIPLE DEMANDS
THE DIFFICULT COMMITMENT
TO SELF-RENUNCIATION.**

Reflection

Much of Julian of Norwich's writing is focused upon the need to cling to—cleave to our loving God. Reflect upon this passage from her work, **Showings** *(p 183).*

"And in this he showed me something small, no bigger than a hazelnut, lying in the palm of my hand, as it seemed to me, and it was as round as a ball. I looked at it with the eye of my understanding and thought: What can this be? I was amazed that it could last, for I thought that because of its littleness it would suddenly have fallen into nothing. And I was answered in my understanding: It lasts and always will, because God loves it; and thus everything has being through the love of God.

"In this little thing I saw three properties. The first is that God made it, the second is that God loves it, the third is that God preserves it. But what did I see in it? It is that God is the Creator and the protector and the lover. For until I am substantially united to him, I can never have perfect rest or true happiness, until, that is, I am so attached to him that there can be no created thing between my God and me."

Questions

1. *How does self-renunciation lead to fuller self-discovery?*

2. *What can you do to foster your own sense of "clinging" to God?*

The Church Says:

The Second Vatican Council cites St. Paul's letter to the Corinthians (1 Cor 7:31), observing that "[a]ll the faithful are invited and obliged to holiness and the perfection of their own state of life. Accordingly let all of them see that they direct their affections rightly, lest they be hindered in their pursuit of perfect love by the use of worldly things and by an adherence to riches which is contrary to the spirit of evangelical poverty, following the apostle's advice: Let those who use this world not fix their abode in it, for the form of this world is passing away. . ." (LG, 42) Worldly things, including our very selves, must be utilized in light of the absolute priority of the kingdom.

The Beatitudes of Jesus urge us to the practice of self-renunciation and to let go of our attachments to the things of this world ("blessed are the poor"). In a sense, the Beatitudes reveal a higher order of happiness and grace, of beauty and peace that cannot be found in worldly goods and status (CCC 2546).

For This Week:

I want to remember:

I want to put my faith into action by:

Questions to Explore

Prayer for the Week

Lord, help me to stop in my haste this week
stop and contemplate the little things
The littleness of a sparrow,
who cannot fall or fly
without your knowing;
The littleness of the ant
who works so hard
for the building of its community;
The littleness of the flower
that does not
worry or toil for its beauty.
For it is in noticing these
little creations of your love,
That I can surmount the courage
to renounce my self into
transformation. Amen.

Twenty-fourth Sunday in Ordinary Time

Scripture:

Exodus 32:7-11, 13, 14
Psalm 51:3-4, 12-13, 17, 19
1 Timothy 1:12-17
Luke 15:1-32 [or 15:1-10]

Focus:

THE CHURCH'S MINISTRY OF RECONCILIATION

Reflection

Directions: *Read slowly and ponder today's readings.*

Questions

1. *How have you experienced reconciliation in your life? (as a child, in your family, with friends, at work)*

2. *There are three parables proclaimed in the Gospel. What does each tell you about God?*

Quotable Quotes

". . . one can therefore sum up the church's mission, rich and complex as it is, as being her central task of reconciling people with God, with themselves, with neighbor, with the whole of creation; and this in a permanent manner since . . . 'the church is also by her nature always reconciling.'"

(John Paul II, *Reconciliatio et Paetentia*, Apostolic Exhortation, 2 december 1984, n.8)

Memorable People

St. John Vianney (1786 1859) grew up during the turbulent years of the French Revolution. He did everything possible to avoid the draft. Although not a gifted student, he was ordained because of his prayerfulness and commitment to ministry. He is known as the Cure of Ars and as an understanding confessor. He heard confessions everyday, sometimes for as long as sixteen hours.

Did You Know?

Reconciliation includes a resolve to change the action or behavior which causes the alienation. Saying "I'm sorry" is only part of reconciliation.

The Church Says:

Reconciliation is a major mission of the Church, given that its founder, Jesus came to restore us to God and thus engaged in a ministry of reconciliation. The mission of Jesus continues in the Church, whom the early Fathers envisioned as the safe boat by which we navigate this unsafe world and a type of Noah's Ark which saves us. Those who are scattered, those who are far off, those who are led astray are invited back to the Church and rediscover unity and salvation.

The Second Vatican Council, referring to Christ who was sent to heal the contrite of heart goes on to say, "Similarly, the Church encompasses with her love all those who are afflicted by human misery and she recognizes in those who are poor and who suffer, the image of her poor and suffering founder . . . The Church, however, clasping sinners to her bosom, at once holy and always in need of purification, follows constantly the path of penance and renewal."

For This Week:

I want to remember:

I want to put my faith into action by:

Questions to Explore

Prayer for the Week

God of our lives, we pray for direction
and steadfastness.
Take away the darkness that sometimes
overshadows us.
Grant us faith that knows no limits,
hope that never fails,
and love that embraces all.
Guide us to know your will and fill us with a
desire to conform our wills to yours.

(Paraphrase of prayer of St. Francis of Assisi)

Twenty-fifth Sunday in Ordinary Time

Scripture:

Amos 8:4-7
Psalm 113:1-2, 4-6, 7-8
1 Timothy 2:1-8
Luke 16:1-13 [or 16:10-13]

Focus:

SOCIAL JUSTICE

Reflection

Directions: *Think of a life experience when you felt you were being cheated or treated unjustly. Describe the circumstances and your feelings. Was there anyone who defended or comforted you*

Questions

1. *How do the readings challenge our culture?*

2. *How do these readings challenge you personally?*

3. *How do you hear yourself being called to respond to the words of Amos?*

Quotable Quotes

St. Catherine of Siena writes from the perspective of God, proclaiming,
". . . I have given many gifts and graces, both spiritual and temporal, with such diversity that I
have not given everything to one single person. . . . I have willed that one should need another
and that all should be my ministers in distributing the graces and gifts that have received from me."
(Catherine of Siena, Dialogues I,7)

Did You Know?

St. John Capistrano (1386-1456) is the patron saint of jurists, perhaps because before joining the
Observant Franciscans in 1415 he studied law and served as a magistrate. After joining the order, he
tirelessly promoted monastic reform in the Franciscan order and elsewhere.

The Church Says:

Each of us, as we are born into this world, are not equipped with everything we need in order to develop bodily or spiritually. We need each other. Differences in individuals are due to age, physical abilities, intellect, moral aptitude, the benefit of social commerce and distribution of wealth (GS 29). Thus, while we are all equally valuable, created in the image and likeness of God, our innate personal gifts are not distributed equally and we are not born into the same social situation and opportunities.

The Catholic position on these differences is that this is part of God's plan. God builds these differences into us so that we are required to receive from others what we need both bodily and spiritually to flourish. Differences among us encourage and oblige persons to practice generosity, kindness, and sharing of goods. On a larger scale, these differences foster the mutual enrichment of cultures (CCC 1937).

For This Week:

I want to remember:

I want to put my faith into action by:

Questions to Explore

Prayer for the Week

*All powerful and ever-living God,
    we sing your praise forever
    and give thanks in all we do
    through Jesus Christ, your son.*

*He witnessed to all a message of justice and peace,
    a message that lives on in our midst
    as a task for us today
    and a promise for tomorrow.*

*We thank you for your blessings of the past,
    and we ask your help for the justice we must
        yet achieve.
Strengthen us as we struggle to bring your justice
    to all your people.*

*We pray in the name of Jesus Christ.
Amen.*

Twenty-sixth Sunday in Ordinary Time

Scripture:

Amos 6:1a, 4-7
Psalm 146:7, 8-9, 9-10
1 Timothy 6:11-16
Luke 16:19-31

Focus:

SOCIAL JUSTICE: PART II

Reflection

Directions: *Think of a social justice issue with which you experience indifference. Name the issue. Explain why you believe you feel indifferent. Do you truly feel indifferent or do have feelings that you do not act on? Describe.*

Questions

1. *What do you believe are the causes of indifference in your own life?*

2. *How do hear yourself being called to concern for the poor and solidarity?*

Did You Know?

John Paul II has upheld St. Peter Claver as a model Christian witness to human solidarity. Peter Claver (1581-1654) was a Spanish Jesuit missionary. He became known as the "saint of the slaves," for at Cartagena, Colombia, his practice was to meet slave ships arriving from Africa and go into their holds, caring for the physical and spiritual good of those who were soon to be slaves. (*Encyclopedia of Catholicism*, p. 989)

The Church Says:

Jesus uses a parable about a wealthy, indifferent man and a poor, needy beggar to teach compassion for others in this world before it is too late and we are judged in the next world. This gospel text relates to our Catholic social teaching on justice and the creation of right relationships in society. Sinful inequalities affect millions of men and women throughout the world. That these inequalities have existed throughout history and in every society does not excuse them. The Catholic Church insists that these unequal conditions between individuals openly contradict the gospel (CCC 1938).

The social teaching of modern popes has contributed to a quantum leap in the Catholic understanding of the role of individuals, groups, and governments in promoting the common good (see Catholic Doctrine, 33 Sunday in Ordinary Time, first paragraph, for a listing of this papal contribution). The Second Vatican Council also teaches, "Their equal dignity as persons demands that we strive for fairer and more humane conditions. Excessive economic and social disparity between individuals and peoples of the one human race is a source of scandal and militates against social justice, equity, human dignity, as well as social and international peace." (GS, 29) But it is not merely a matter of material goods and their just distribution. It is also a matter of spreading spiritual goods of the faith.

For This Week:

I want to remember:

I want to put my faith into action by:

Questions to Explore

Prayer for the Week

Micah 6:8

He has told you, O mortal, what is good;

and what does the Lord require of you

but to do justice, and to love kindness,

and to walk humbly with your God?

Scripture:

Habakkuk 1:2-3; 2:2-4
Psalm 95:1-2, 6-7, 8-9
2 Timothy 1:6-8, 13-14
Luke 17:5-10

Focus:

SACRAMENT OF HOLY ORDERS

Reflection

1. *When have you felt like a servant? What was difficult for you? What was life-giving for you? Write down your experience of being a servant.*

2. *Draw a line, and put 1 at one end and 10 at the other end. Evaluate how you see yourself on a scale of 1 to 10, with 10 being high, in terms of total commitment as a disciple and place an x at the corresponding place on the line. Then, describe a way God is asking you to give more of yourself over to God.*

3. *List three ways you see yourself as a minister to others, either in preparation for your baptism, or rooted in your baptism. Describe how you sense God inviting you to be an apostle to others as a married or single person? Would you ever consider becoming a priest or deacon, or encouraging someone you know to pursue this vocation? Why or why not?*

Quotable Quotes

"Write the vision; make it plain on tablets, so that a runner may read it. For there is still a vision for the appointed time; it speaks of the end, and does not lie. If it seems to tarry, wait for it; it will surely come, it will not delay." Habakkuk 2:2, 3

"[J]oin with me in suffering for the gospel, relying on the power of God, who saved us and called us with a holy calling." 2 Timothy 1:8, 9

"We are useless slaves; we have done only what we ought to have done." Luke 17:10

Memorable People

Archbishop Oscar Romero of El Salvador was assassinated for his work with the poor. His story is portrayed in the movie *Romero*.

Joseph Cardinal Bernardin, who died November 14, 1996, forgave his public accuser.

Pope Leo the Great in 452 persuaded Attila the Hun not to invade the Italian peninsula. His ringing affirmation of baptism, "Christian, remember your dignity!" is remembered in the office of readings for Christmas Day.

Pope John XXIII is well known for convening Vatican Council II in 1963, and for his peace encyclical, *Pacem in Terris* (Peace on Earth).

Did You Know?

The bishop's chair is called cathedra and is the source of the word cathedral. This chair refers to the teaching office of the bishop.

The imposition of hands is the primary action in the ordination rite.

The oil of chrism used in the ordination of bishops, priests, and deacons is also used for infant baptism with reference to Christ anointed as priest, prophet, and king, and in Confirmation.

Today the church has permanent deacons as well as deacons who will be ordained priests.

The Church Says:

All who are baptized into Christ are joined to his priesthood. The apostles, whose name refers to being both a witness of Christ and being sent on mission for the gospel, continued the priestly work of Christ. In the early church both a charismatic leadership based on gifts of the Spirit in Corinth and an ordained leadership which developed with the three ministries of bishop, priest, and deacon. From the time of the apostles with no break in succession, the church continues to ordain people for these three ministries. All share in the ministry of the bishop, who is given the role of guarding and teaching the faith of the church, and shepherding the people. The imposition of hands is the essential gesture of the rite of ordination. Today the church ordains permanent deacons for service and some liturgical functions, as well as deacons who will be ordained priests, called transitional deacons.

For This Week:

I want to remember:

I want to put my faith into action by:

Questions to Explore

Prayer for the Week

God, through your Spirit
you stir into flame God's gift of faith in me.
Make me your humble servant.
May I live my life in service of your gospel,
until you reign in all parts of my city and world.
Give me strength when I encounter difficulties.
Give me a compassionate heart when I get hurt.
Give me hope when I feel discouraged.
Most of all, give me a love for you,
your people, and your gospel. Amen.

Scripture:

2 Kings 5:14-17
Psalm 98:1, 2-3, 3-4
2 Timothy 2:8-13
Luke 17:11-19

Focus:

PRAYER OF THANKSGIVING

Reflection

Directions: *Read Luke's Gospel 4:1-13*

Questions

1. *In what ways have you been like the other nine lepers? They asked Jesus for healing and forgot to return to give thanks.*

2. *In what ways are you like the one leper who does return to give thanks to Jesus for granting your petition?*

Quotable Quotes

In all circumstances give thanks, for this is the will of God for you in Christ Jesus." 1 Thessalonians 5:18

"Devote yourselves to prayer, keeping alert in it with thanksgiving . . ." Colossians 4:2

Did You Know?

"Eucharist" is a Greek word meaning thanksgiving. Each Mass is a prayer of thanksgiving addressed to God.

In the introductory dialogue to the beginning of the Liturgy of Eucharist, we pray: "Let us give thanks to the Lord our God. It is right to give him thanks and praise." (*Roman Missal*, The Order of Mass, Eucharistic Prayer.)

The Church Says:

Our Catholic tradition names five basic types of prayer:
Blessing and adoration
Petition
Intercession
Thanksgiving
Praise.

Any particular moment of prayer between an individual or group and God may very well move between these various types. The Scriptures for this Sunday vividly illustrate the prayer of thanksgiving.

All of life and creation is a gift from God. How much more is the gift given to us in Christ by which life and creation is redeemed and set free from sin and its wages. The whole stance of the Church, therefore, is one of thanksgiving for God's saving action in Jesus.

The greatest gift is the life, ministry, suffering and death of Jesus.

For This Week:

I want to remember:

I want to put my faith into action by:

Questions to Explore

Prayer for the Week

God, we give you thanks for the gift of life
for the people who have nurtured our lives
and helped us to know of your marvelous love;
for all creation, the great and the small;
for the gift of freedom which allows us to say yes
to the gift of faith;
for the gift of reconciliation which allows us to
be generous in forgiving one another.
God, you are the great gift of love. Thank you.

Scripture:

Exodus 17:8-13
Psalm 121:1-2, 3-4, 5-6, 7-8
2 Timothy 3:14-4:2
Luke 18:1-8

Focus:

PRAYER: PETITION AND INTERCESSION

Reflection

1. *Describe some experiences you've had of asking for something more than once with a favorable result. Describe your feelings during the time of asking, and when receiving the result.*

2. *What happens in your relationship with God when you ask God for things? Look back over your experiences and notice feelings and changes in you. Write down your insights.*

3. *Write down your beliefs about prayer using the following points as helps:*

   Describe how posture, e.g., sitting, standing, kneeling, head bowed, hands open, or outstretched arms affects your prayer. What prayer postures are comfortable for you?

   When you ask God for something, do you expect to get it? What do you believe about the power of prayer?

   What happens inside you when you pray?

Quotable Quotes

"Ask, and it will be given you; search, and you will find; knock, and the door will be opened for you." Matthew 7:7

Likewise the Spirit helps us in our weakness; for we do not know how to pray as we ought, but that Spirit intercedes with sighs too deep for words. Romans 8:26

Memorable People

St. Monica, whose feast is celebrated August 27, prayed many years for the conversion of her son, St. Augustine, whose feast is celebrated August 28.

Did You Know?

Cloisters religious congregations, e.g., the Carmelites and the Cistercians, have prayer as their primary ministry.

St. Ignatius Loyola, known for his Spiritual Exercises, believed that the true desires of the heart are God-given, and that God, who respects and gives freedom, waits for the person to pray these desires. When praying these desires, the person moves into closer relationship with God.

A popular form of prayer is the novena (Latin for nine) which is a series of nine successive times of prayer, e.g., on nine Mondays. Novenas are often prayed because of special intentions.

The Church Says:

Intercessory prayer and petitionary prayer are two forms of prayer in our Catholic tradition. This type of prayer brings as awareness that as human beings we are limited and in need of what God can provide. Christian petition is prayed with the concern that in Gods response the kingdom of God come about. Intercessions are usually prayed on behalf of others. Bringing our own needs to God in petition and praying for others through intercession joins us with Christ, who intercedes for us. The prayer posture of praying with outstretched arms makes us vulnerable and open to God's response.

For This Week:

I want to remember:

I want to put my faith into action by:

Questions to Explore

Prayer for the Week

Sit with the palms of your hands facing upward before you. Notice what your heart desires from God. Tell God each of these desires in your own words. End with this prayer:

God I bring you the desires of my heart.
Draw me always closer to you.
I place in your hands all for whom I care
and who need your help.
Hear my prayer through the Holy Spirit.
Amen.

Thirtieth Sunday in Ordinary Time

Scripture:

Sirach 35:12-14, 16-18
Psalm 34:2-3, 17-18, 19, 23
2 Timothy 4:6-8, 16-18
Luke 18:9-14

Focus:

PRAYER: HUMILITY BEFORE GOD

Reflection

Directions: *In the first column list your religious attitudes which may be self-centered and egotistical and ways that you compare yourself to others. In the second column list your religious qualities or attitudes which are sincere and humble.*

SELF-CENTERED	SINCERE

Questions

1. *How would you describe authentic humility?*

2. *Where would you like to improve your inner disposition toward prayer?*

Quotable Quotes

"For me, prayer is a surge of the heart; it is a simple look turned toward heaven, it is a cry of recognition and of love, embracing both trial and joy."

(St. Therese, *Manuscrits autobiographiques*, C 25r)

Did You Know?

The traditional postures for prayer are standing and kneeling. The former derives from our forebears in faith, the Jews who stood with hands outstretched as a sign of reverence and humility—their open hands contained nothing and were to be filled by God. The latter derives from the medieval court as a sign of respect and humility where one's hands were folded and placed within one's liege to whom faithfulness was pledged.

The Church Says:

Prayer raises our mind and heart to God, but that which is raised is not ourselves. In other words, believers pray not out of pride or willfulness but from the depths of a contrite and humble heart. Thus, humility is the foundation of and basic stance of prayer (CCC 2559).

In prayer we receive not ourselves but what is being offered to us by God in Christ. St. Paul uses the image of being poured out in the second reading for this Sunday and in the parable of Jesus, true prayer is illustrated by the individual who speaks humble words sincerely. In the gospel of John, Jesus exclaims to the Samaritan woman, "If you knew the gift of God!" (Jn 4:10) The amazing nature of authentic praying is that God offers us everything we need in prayer. Indeed, the Lord seeks us out in prayer, thirsts for us. Prayer becomes the encounter of God's thirst with ours. The divine love of the Most High thirsts that we, in turn, may thirst for God (CCC 2560). Humility enables one to approach the life-giving waters that God offers us in the sacrifice of Jesus who says to us, "I am thirsty." (Jn 19:28)

For This Week:

I want to remember:

I want to put my faith into action by:

Questions to Explore

Prayer for the Week

Prayer of Thomas Merton

My Lord God, I have no idea where I am going. I do not see the road ahead of me. I cannot know for certain where it will end. Nor do I really know myself, and the fact that I think that I am following your will does not mean that I am actually doing so. But I believe that the desire to please you does in fact please you. And I hope I have that desire in all that I am doing. I hope that I will never do anything apart from that desire. And I know that as I do this you will lead me by the right road though I may know nothing about it. Therefore will I trust you always though I may seem to be lost and in the shadow of death. I will not fear, for you are ever with me, and you will never leave me to face my perils alone.

Thirty-first Sunday in Ordinary Time

Scripture:

Wisdom 11:22-12:2
Psalm 145:1-2, 8-9, 10-11, 13-14
2 Thessalonians 1:11-2:2
Luke 19:1-10

Focus:

JUSTIFICATION

Reflection

Directions: *What would Jesus see if he was invited into your home, that is, your heart and your mind? Is there anything that you would want to rearrange, fix up, hide, showcase? How do you believe Jesus would respond to the truth about your "home?"*

Questions

1. *Jesus waits to be received into our "homes." Are you ready to receive him?*

2. *Is there a risk in welcoming Jesus into our lives? Explain.*

Quotable Quotes

Julian of Norwich (1342-1416), who devoted herself to strict solitude and penitential works, received a series of sixteen mystical visions in 1373. Her writings today have attracted new interest. She describes one of her visions in terms similar to the reading from Wisdom. "and in this he showed me something small, no bigger than a hazelnut, lying in the palm of my hand, as it seemed to me, and it was as round as a ball. I looked at it with the eye of my understanding and thought: What can this be? I was amazed that it could last, for I thought that because of its littleness it would suddenly fallen into nothing. And I was answered in my understanding: It lasts and always will because God loves it; and thus everything has being through the love of God."
(*Julian of Norwich: Showings*, ed. Edmund Colledge, OSA and James Walsh, S.J., Paulist Press, New York, 1978, p. 183)

Did You Know?

Catholic culture has tended to emphasize the unworthiness of humans to receive God's favor—sentiment expressed in popular devotion through prayers and hymns, such as, "Lord, I am Not Worthy" (a favorite of the generation before Vatican II). At the same time, Catholics have always affirmed that real holiness is possible for human beings, and can be sought through prayer, good works, and the sacraments.

The Church Says:

Our Catholic understanding is that justification is God's saving action in Jesus by the Holy Spirit which frees us from sin and renews us. Justification, in short, opens the way to salvation by good works through the community of the faithful, the church. Those who are justified are cleansed from sin and put in a right relationship with God. For us believers, this happens in the gift of baptism (CCC 1987).

The Protestant reformers emphasized the universality of sin, the absolute gratuity of justification and insisted that human freedom was destroyed by original sin. The Council of Trent rejected this view. Instead, the Church proclaimed that it was possible to cooperate with God's grace and to be renewed inwardly. It is possible to grow in holiness and we practice the virtues of hope and love, moving toward eternal life and increasing grace within ourselves by our good works. Unfortunately, the way in which the Catholic Church and the Reformation theologians initially spoke about justification only furthered the split in Christianity. Today, there is a much closer agreement on the basic themes of justification: God justifies by grace alone, through the saving action of Jesus Christ, and individuals appropriate that justification by their faith-in-action. The area in which the differences exist today is in our focus on God's saving activity through the Church and the sacraments as celebrated and lived.

For This Week:

I want to remember:

I want to put my faith into action by:

Questions to Explore

Prayer for the Week

Lord,
Creator and Redeemer of your holy people,
your great love has drawn me to seek and find you.
Look upon me today,
purify my heart,
and bring to fulfillment in me the plan of your grace,
so that, faithfully following Christ,
I may come to drink the waters of salvation.
I ask this through Christ our Lord.
Amen.

(adapted from Prayers of Exorcism from the Rite of Christian Initiation of Adults, p.47.)

Scripture:

2 Maccabees 7:1-2, 9-14
Psalm 17:1, 5-6, 8, 15
2 Thessalonians 2:16–3:5
Luke 20:27-38 [or 20:27, 34-38]

Focus:

HEAVEN AND HELL

Reflection

Directions: *In both the Apostles ' Creed and the Nicene Creed, believers profess resurrection of the body and life everlasting. Read slowly and ponder the first reading 2 Maccabees 7:1-2, 9-14 and the Gospel, Luke 20:27-38.*

Questions

1. *Resurrection is . . .*

2. *Heaven is . . .*

3. *Hell is . . .*

Quotable Quotes

"How great will your glory and happiness be, to be allowed to see God, to be honored with sharing the joy of salvation and eternal light with Christ your Lord and God . . . to delight in the joy of immortality in the Kingdom of heaven with the righteous."
(St. Cyprian of Carthage, Epistulae, 58,10, 1:CSEL 3/2.665)

Did You Know?

The groups that often entered into debate with Jesus were the Sadducees and the Pharisees. The Sadducees accepted only the Torah, the first five books of the Bible. They believed neither in angels nor in the resurrection of the dead. The Pharisees accepted the Torah as well as subsequent books of the Hebrew (Old Testament) Scripture. They also believed in life after death.

Beatific Vision is the term used to describe seeing God face-to-face.

The Church Says:

Heaven is the mode of existence for those who are eternally blessed. We believe that those who die in the Lord, who die in grace and friendship with God and who are perfectly purified live for ever in the blessedness of the beatific vision.

Hell is the mode of existence for those who are eternally damned. Jesus warns that if we do not meet the needs of the hungry and the thirsty, if we do not welcome the stranger, clothe the naked, care for the ill, and visit the imprisoned we will be excluded from his presence and be cast into hell. Those who die in the state of mortal sin without repentance are separated from God by their own free choice. This state of final and eternal self-exclusion from union with God is termed hell.

No one is predestined. Indeed, God is a loving God and acts to save all.

For This Week:

I want to remember:

I want to put my faith into action by:

Questions to Explore

Prayer for the Week

All powerful God,
By your power we were given life,
By your power and in your providence
we live our lives,
You set us free from sin and death through
the saving death of your son, Jesus,
we look forward to the day when we will see
you face to face. Amen.

Thirty-third Sunday in Ordinary Time

Scripture:

Malachi 3:19-20a
Psalm 98:5-6, 7-8, 9
2 Thessalonians 3:7-12
Luke 21:5-19

Focus:

JUSTICE

Reflection

Directions: *We have hints of God's Justice happening in our world. Hints of forgiveness, hope, and love. Review your past week for signs of God's Reign in your world.*

Questions

1. *When have you felt called to be an agent of God's reign in your family . . . at work?*

2. *Who are the people you have met over the years who are signs of God's reign of Justice?*

Quotable Quotes

In the often quoted words of Pope Paul VI:
"If you want peace, work for justice."

Did You Know?

The virtue of justice has been symbolized in artwork by the convention of a woman, crowned and wearing a blindfold, holding scales or a sword, or both. The scales are pre-Christian in origin, but the sword may well derive from the *Sol Justitiae*, that is Christ with a sword and scales as represented in an engraving by Durer, dating from the late 1490s. A statue of a blindfolded woman, scales in one hand and sword in the other, can be seen standing above the dome of the Old Bailey, which houses the Royal Courts of Justice in London.
(*The Oxford Companion to Christian Art and Architecture*, Peter and Linda Murray, Oxford University Press, 1996, p. 264.)

The Church Says:

The word "justice" is derived from a Latin root *ius*, which means "right." Pursuing justice means pursuing other's rights and the duties flowing from those rights. For example, the duty that obligates one to respect another's body flows from the other's right to the fullness of life. Pope John XXIII outlined basic human rights in *Pacem Terris* (11 April 1963, n. 11-45) as the right to life and a worthwhile manner of living, the right which respects one's person regardless of sex, ethnic background, religion or nationality, the right to freely pursue and express the truth, the right to basic education, the right to worship, the right to gainful work, decent working conditions and proper compensation, the right to meet and associate, and the right to emigrate (Richard P. McBrien, *Catholicism*, New Edition, HarperSan Francisco, p. 944).

Justice as envisioned here, is not meted out by our courtrooms and civil proceedings. It is a quality of faithful persons who love God and love their neighbor. It is not the retribution of the Old Testament scripture, taking an eye for an eye, but the "words and the wisdom" promised by Jesus (his words in today's gospel) to those who stand firmly and equitably in the midst of trying times.

For This Week:

I want to remember:

I want to put my faith into action by:

Questions to Explore

Prayer for the Week

Psalm 85

You have favored, O Lord your land;
you have restored the well-being
of Jacob.
You have forgiven the guilt of your people;
you have covered all their sins.
You have withdrawn all your wrath;
you have revoked your burning anger.
Restore us, O God our savior,
and abandon your displeasure
against us.
Will you be ever angry with us,
prolonging your anger to all
generations?
Will you not instead give us life;
and shall not your people rejoice in you?
Show us, O Lord, your kindness,
and grant us your salvation.

I will hear what God proclaims;
the Lord—for he proclaims peace:
to his people, and to his faithful ones,
and to those who put in him their hope.
Near indeed is his salvation to those who
fear him,
glory dwelling in our land.
Kindness and truth shall meet;
justice and peace shall kiss.
Truth shall spring out of the earth,
and justice shall look down
from heaven.
The Lord himself will give his benefits;
our land shall yield its increase.
Justice shall walk before him,
and salvation, along the way of his steps.

Thirty-fourth Sunday in Ordinary Time

Scripture:

2 Samuel 5:1-3
Psalm 122:1-2, 3-4, 4-5
Colossians 1:12-20
Luke 23:35-43

Focus:

CHRIST THE KING

Reflection

Directions: *Read slowly and ponder the readings for today.*

Questions

1. *Contrast the kingship of Christ with the kingship of David.*

2. *What kind of king were some Israelites expecting? How would Jesus' kingdom differ from their expectations?*

3. *What do expect the kingdom of God to be?*

The Church Says:

Catholic teaching asserts that Christ's lordship extends over all of human history (CCD 450) and that he reigns above every earthly power and principality (CCC 668). What does this mean? First, this means that Jesus Christ is the redeemer of all people. Past, present and future generations are offered salvation on the one who by his suffering, death and resurrection has achieved what we could never achieve on our own. Second, no earthly reality or person is above Jesus; he reigns supreme and everything and everyone is subject to the power of his saving love and goodness.

Jesus, the Lord, also reigns supreme over the Church, which considers Christ its head (CCC 792). The Second Vatican Council taught, "[T]he Church, endowed with the gifts of her founder and faithfully observing his precepts of charity, humility and self-denial, receives the mission of proclaiming and establishing among all peoples the kingdom of Christ and of God, and she is, on earth, the seed and the beginning of that kingdom. While she slowly grows to maturity, the Church longs for the completed kingdom and, with all her strength, hopes and desires to be united in glory with her king." (LG, 5) Thus, the Church is not to be confused with the kingdom. The Church, rather, serves the kingdom.

For This Week:

I want to remember:

I want to put my faith into action by:

Questions to Explore

Prayer for the Week

To Jesus Christ, our sovereign king,
we give you thanks and praise.
To you, all creation bows down
in humble homage.
In you, we place all our faith,
all our hope, all our love.
Empty our hearts of anger, bitterness
and doubt.
Fill them with the peace you alone can give.
Make us eager to continue your work,
that through it you will reign over the
hearts of all people. Amen.

HOLY DAYS AND FEASTS

Immaculate Conception

Scripture:

Genesis 3:9-15, 20
Psalm 98:1, 2-3, 3-4
Ephesians 1:3-6, 11-12
Luke 1:26-38

Focus:

IMMACULATE CONCEPTION OF MARY

Reflection

Directions: A Magnificat is a Hebrew prayer form that expresses praise and petition to the God of love. In the space below write your own Magnificat. In it express your praise of God for each of the 'favors' or graces freely given to you by God, without your merit or worthiness. Write of your own weakness and fear and ask God to lift you out of these frailties.

Quotable Quotes

Paul VI in his Guidelines for Devotion to the Blessed Virgin Mary (1974) stipulates,
"The ultimate purpose of devotion to the Blessed Virgin is
to glorify God and lead Christians to commit themselves to a life
which conforms absolutely to his will."

Memorable People

In the middle of the 19th century, **Catherine Laboure** of France had a vision of Mary standing on a globe, crushing the serpent, with rays of light coming from her hands. Around her were the words, "O Mary conceived without sin, pray for us who have recourse to thee." By 1832 this vision led to the crafting of a medal, one side of which depicted Mary as she appeared in Catherine's vision and the other etched with the letter, 'M,' under which were twin hearts—Jesus encircled with a crown of thorns and Mary's pierced with a sword. Surrounding the whole are twelve stars. Many miracles accompanied devotion to this title of Mary and the wearing of the medal became popular. **Bernadette Soubirous** in Lourdes, France, just two decades later, saw a vision of a lady who called herself the "Immaculate Conception." Lourdes likewise has become known as a place of miraculous healing and pilgrimage.

Did You Know?

In 1846 the bishops of the United States chose Mary under the title of the Immaculate Conception to be the patroness of this relatively new country.

The Church Says:

Since the eighth century in the East, and the eleventh century in the West, the Christian church has set aside a day to celebrate Mary's conception in the womb of her mother, who is in tradition called Anne, thus indicating a reverence for Mary's whole person. The church did not define the dogma of the Immaculate Conception, however, until the mid-nineteenth century.

This feast celebrates that Mary was conceived without sin. In 1954 Pope Pius XII articulated this understanding of Mary's Immaculate Conception: Mary was free from any stain of original sin from the moment of her conception. This article of faith, declared by the Pope, was expressed as an infallible dogma and was the result of years of reflection and consideration by the Church. Although not stated explicitly in the scriptures, it relies on a very ancient tradition concerning Mary.

For This Feast:

I want to remember:

I want to put my faith into action by:

Questions to Explore

Prayer for this Feast

O God, source of all life,
thank you for the gift of Mary,
mother of Jesus.
You honored this woman
from the moment of her conception
she is your highly favored daughter,
conceived without sin;
bearer of your beloved Son;
mother of our salvation.
Her simple 'yes' to your holy will,
her trusting heart,
opened the way for our salvation.
O Mary, conceived without sin
pray for us as we open ourselves
to the will of your divine Son.

Solemnity of Mary, Mother of God

Scripture:

Numbers 6:22-27
Psalm 67:2-3, 5, 6, 8
Galatians 4:4-7
Luke 2:16-21

Focus:

MARY, MOTHER OF GOD

Reflection

Directions: *From the gospel and the teaching on Mary, Mother of God, select three to five characteristics or qualities visible in her. When you have finished, next to Mary's quality, write a short, concrete description of how you could imitate that quality in your own life.*

Questions

1. *How does the model of Mary challenge you as you seek to bear Christ for the world?*

2. *How can you, as a believer, become more a part of God's saving plan?*

Quotable Quotes

"In celebrating this annual cycle of the mysteries of Christ, Holy Church honors the Blessed Mary, Mother of God, with a special love. She is inseparably linked with the saving work of her Son. In her the Church admires and exults the most excellent fruit of redemption and joyfully contemplates, as in a faultless image, that which she herself desires and hopes wholly to be."

(SC 103)

Did You Know?

This is a multi-layered feast day. While Roman Catholics celebrate Mary, Mother of God on this day, the Lutheran and Episcopalian churches celebrate the Holy Name of Jesus. The Byzantine Church celebrates this as the feast of the Circumcision of Jesus. Pope Paul VI also asked "all people of good will" to observe the World Day of Peace on January 1 without changing or ignoring the designation of this day as celebrating Mary, Mother of God.

The Church Says:

On this first day of January, between Christmas and Epiphany, the Church gathers to contemplate the Paschal Mystery through this celebration focused on Mary, Mother of God.

The Second Vatican Council observed that "In celebrating this annual cycle of the mysteries of Christ, Holy Church honors the Blessed Mary, Mother of God, with a special love. She is inseparably linked with the saving work of her Son. In her the Church admires and exults the most excellent fruit of redemption and joyfully contemplates, as in a faultless image, that which she herself desires and hopes wholly to be." (SC 103)

She is thus linked to the saving work of Jesus because she is not merely passively engaged by God. Mary freely cooperates in the work of our salvation through faith and obedience.

For This Feast:

I want to remember:

I want to put my faith into action by:

Questions to Explore

Prayer for this Feast

God, you have sent your Son, Jesus
to dwell among your people.
Like us in all ways, except sin,
he was carried and born
of the womb of Mary.
Marvelous are your works, O God!
Mary, Mother of God,
because of your faith and obedience
you gave birth to the Savior,
the Counselor,
the Prince of Peace.
Blessings and honor are yours, Mary!
For by your openness to God
the Creator became human
and won our salvation.
Grant us the grace to hear
to believe
to follow
your Word made flesh.
Amen.

The Presentation of the Lord

Scripture:

Malachi 3:1-4
Psalm 24:7, 8, 9, 10
Hebrews 2:14-18
Luke 2:22-40 [or 2:22-32]

Focus:

JESUS IS HUMAN AND DIVINE.

Reflection

Directions: *As you listen to the gospel from Luke 2:22-40, place yourself in the position of Simeon, Anna and Jesus' parents. Then, in the three columns below indicate what each of these characters in the account reveals to you about the nature of Jesus.*

SIMEON	ANNA	MARY and JOSEPH

Questions

1. *What about the nature of Jesus been revealed to you through the people and the circumstances of your life?*

2. *In the light of the observations of these holy people and your own experience, who is Jesus?*

Did You Know?

In the Northern Hemisphere this feast is celebrated in the dead of winter darkness. The assembly gathers prior to the liturgy outside the church and candles are blessed. As these blessed candles are lit, the people process into church singing and the Mass of the Presentation of the Lord is celebrated. Customarily, enough candles are blessed on this day in order to last through the year. Thus this feast also goes by the name "Candlemas."

The Church Says:

The Catholic Church confesses belief in Jesus, the second person of the Trinity, as possessing two natures. That is, Jesus Christ is fully human and fully divine. While this is based in the apostles' experience of him and is asserted by Scripture, the theological understanding of this doctrine was first addressed by the Council of Chalcedon in 451 due to the Monophysite controversy (or heresy). The Monophysites charged that the human nature of Christ ceased to exist when the divine person of the Son of God assumed it. (The doctrine section for the Fourth Sunday of Easter treats of the divinity of Christ.)

The Council of Chalcedon proclaimed, "Following the holy Father, we unanimously teach and confess one and the same Son, our Lord Jesus Christ: the same perfect in divinity and perfect in humanity, the same truly God and truly man, composed of rational soul and body; consubstantial with the Father as to his divinity and consubstantial with us as to his humanity; 'like us in all things but sin.'" The Council then answered the Monophysites and asserted, "We confess that one and the same Christ . . .is to be acknowledged in two natures without confusion, change, division, or separation. The distinction between the natures was never abolished by their union, but rather the character proper to each of the two natures was preserved as they came together in one person. . ." (Council of Chalcedon, DS 301-02)

Another way the Church expresses this is to assert that Jesus is both the Son of God and the Son of the Virgin Mary. The two natures of Christ, one divine and one human, are not confused, but united. They are united in the one person of Jesus Christ. This union does not cease

For This Feast:

I want to remember:

I want to put my faith into action by:

Questions to Explore

Prayer for this Feast

Jesus, we desire to be messengers of your Good News. There are many in this world who need to hear the message of your human and divine presence with us. In your humanity, you have walked with us, felt the pains and joys of living and have loved much. In your divinity, you are our source of sustenance and transformation. We raise up to you not only ourselves, but those whose names be presented to this circle of prayer. You, who promised to be with us as we gather, have heard our cry. Give us the courage to share all that you have come to mean in our lives. Give us the words to speak the glory of your presence and promise—Son of God and Child of Mary. Prepare the hearts of those we bring before you that they might hear all that you have accomplished in your living, dying and rising. Amen.

The Ascension of the Lord

Scripture:

Acts 1:1-11
Psalm 47:2-3, 6-7, 8-9
Hebrews 9:24-28; 10:19-23
   [or Ephesians 1:17-23]
Luke 24:46-53

Focus:

THE ASCENSION OF THE LORD

Worksheet

1. *What do you feel as you picture Jesus ascending to heaven?*

2. *What does the ascension mean for you?*

3. *What are the signs of God's ongoing presence in your personal life?*

Quotable Quotes

"Jesus Christ . . . has gone into heaven and is at the right hand of God, with angels, authorities, and powers made subject to him." (1 Peter 3:22)

"He was lifted up, and a cloud took him out of their sight . . . Why do you stand looking up toward heaven? This Jesus, who has been taken up from you into heaven, will come in the same way as you saw him go into heaven." (Acts 1:9, 11)

Did You Know?

The feast of the Ascension was celebrated from the later years of the fourth century. The celebration in the early years included a procession to the Mount of Olives, where the Ascension is said to have occurred.

The Church Says:

The risen Christ, 40 days after the Resurrection, ascended into heaven. The ascension was witnessed by the Apostles. The Ascension closes the post-Resurrection appearances. Christ left this world in bodily form so that the Spirit that was promised could come. Christ ascended by his own power into heaven. In a new way the work of the church was begun, to be empowered by the Spirit on Pentecost. Christ's time on earth in physical form began with Mary's agreement to become his mother, and ended with the Ascension. The Church symbolically views Jesus as sitting in majesty at God's right hand. The Church awaits the Second Coming of Christ, when all of human history will be brought under his authority.

For This Feast:

I want to remember:

I want to put my faith into action by:

Questions to Explore

Prayer for this Feast

Lord Jesus, you ascended in glory.

You are my hope.

May I follow you into the new creation.

Until that time may I have the joy of experiencing

your presence with me as you promised. Amen.

Scripture:

Proverbs 8:22-31
Psalm 8:4-5, 6-7, 8-9
Romans 5:1-5
John 16:12-15

THE TRINITY

Reflection Questions

1. *What is your experience of each of the persons of the Trinity—Father, Son, and Holy Spirit?*

2. *What does it mean to you for God to be a trinity of persons?*

3. *Give qualities and names you associate with each of the persons of the Trinity. Think of Old Testament times, New Testament times, and post-testament times.*

Quotable Quotes

Before his ascension, Jesus said:

"Go therefore and make disciples of all nations,

baptizing them in the name of the Father and of the Son and of the Holy Spirit."

Matthew 28:19.

Did You Know?

St. Patrick used the shamrock to teach about the Trinity.
The trinitarian formula, "In the name of the Father, and of the Son, and of the Holy Spirit," is used to begin and end the prayer of the Mass, as well as many other prayers. Christians often bless themselves with the sign of the cross when using this formula.

The Church Says:

There is one God and three persons, the Father, the Son, and the Holy Spirit. This mystery of the Trinity is central to Christian faith and life. Throughout salvation history God reveals God's nature as these three persons of the Trinity. The three persons of God always existed. The second person of the Trinity took on a human nature in Jesus. Though all three persons, God always existed and participated in human history. Matthew's Gospel states that Jesus commands that people be baptized "in the name of the Father, and of the Son, and of the Holy Spirit." (Matthew 28:19) The first ecumenical council at Nicaea in 325 named the Son's equality with God. The second ecumenical council at Constantinople in 381 named the Spirit's equality with the Father and the Son. This formulation is professed by the church each Sunday in the Creed. The love of God is expressed between and among the persons of the trinity in equality and unity. This trinitarian God gives meaning to human relationships of love.

For This Feast:

I want to remember:

I want to put my faith into action by:

Questions to Explore

Prayer for this Feast

In the name of the Father, and of the Son,
and of the Holy Spirit.
God, in your three persons, I praise you.
Let me come to know you more in your
creative energy, in your dying and rising,
and in your powerful and gentle movements.
May I know your love in the love I experience
and share with my sisters and brothers.
Amen.

The Body and Blood of Christ

Scripture:

Genesis 14:18-20
Psalm 110:1, 2, 3, 4
1 Corinthians 11:23-26
Luke 9:11b-17

Focus:

THE REAL PRESENCE OF JESUS IN THE EUCHARIST

Reflection

She heaved her large frame onto the bus,
pregnant and laden with packages
she noticed with dismay all the seats were taken.
The man, over eighty, palsied arms beckoned,
he stood and offered his seat.
He was eucharist!

The young child fumbled through his pockets,
one dime short, for the long awaited ice cream cone.
The clerk noticed his sad, frantic eyes,
 offered the needed coin from her own pocket.
She was eucharist!

He spent his days pecking through garbage,
looking for the treasure—
aluminum cans, redeemable for pennies.

Crowds hustled by, staring, jostling and fearing him
for his appearance was strange.
But he always took time to return their stares with a big smile
and a good morning—good day, greeting.
He was eucharist!

The new secretary at the law office
panicked at the computer's non-cooperation.
Her frenzied keyboard mania was evident
to the senior law partner, about to rush through
the door for an important hearing.
He backtracked, and offered his help,
reassuring and calming jangled nerves.
He was eucharist!

Questions

1. *From this brief meditation, how can you be eucharist in your ordinary life?*

2. *What are some other ways you have seen eucharist operative at work or in your family?*

Quotable Quotes

"You give them something to eat." (Luke 9:13)

Did You Know?

Benediction (from the Latin for "blessing") is a liturgical service wherein the consecrated host, the Body of Christ, is displayed in a special container called a monstrance or ostensorium. Catholics pray before and adore the sacred species—based on our belief that the bread therein is no longer merely bread but the Body of Christ.

The Church Says:

We believe that when the Church gathers, Mass is celebrated with the Liturgy of the Word and the Liturgy of the Eucharist, and within the Eucharist, bread and wine are presented and prayed over, the Spirit of God descends and makes those elements into the body and blood of Jesus Christ. The Church has insisted from the earliest times that this is the "real presence" of Christ, that is, real in the fullest sense a substantial presence by which Christ, both God and man, makes himself wholly and entirely present (CCC 1374). Why? Most especially because Jesus himself promised this and secondarily because the apostles and those who have followed in this Church have experienced it to be so.

The substantial change that takes place within the elements of bread and wine are a conversion. Indeed, the term in our tradition for the change which takes place is "transubstantiation" (CCC 1376).

This eucharistic presence of Christ continues as long as the eucharistic species (the bread and wine) subsist. We also believe that the real presence of Jesus experienced wholly and totally in each of the elements, such that while an individual consumes only the eucharistic bread both body and blood are received and if only the eucharistic wine is consumed both body and blood of Christ are received (CCC 1377). In connection with the celebration of the Eucharist, the Church also teaches that at Mass Christ is recognized and experienced in the assembly of people who gather, in the person of the presider, in the proclamation of the Word and in the eucharistic species (GIRM, Chapter 1, n 7)

For This Feast:

I want to remember:

I want to put my faith into action by:

Questions to Explore

Prayer for this Feast

*Body of Christ, open me to
Your whole body—
the People of God.
Blood of Christ, cleanse me
from all sin and wrongdoing
both inside and out.*

*I ask that your presence in the eucharist
be a sign to me of
our covenant of love;
won through sacrifice and suffering.*

*May the Eucharist inspire me to become
a sign of your presence in the world
as I make myself present to others.*

The Birth of John the Baptist

Scripture:

Isaiah 49:1-6
Psalm 139:1-3, 13-14, 14-15
Acts 13:22-26
Luke 1:57-66, 80

Focus:

JOHN THE BAPTIST GAVE HIS LIFE TO PREPARING THE WAY FOR CHRIST.

Reflection

1. What are some of your feelings about God's action or important stories around the birth a child in your family?

2. What begins to happen in people as a result of Zechariah's being struck mute and then finding his speech at the time of the naming of John.

3. What newness is God initiating in you? Be more specific in your example than being part of this process to become Catholic.

4. Make a timeline of John the Baptist's life and put on it all the things you know about John the Baptist.

5. What kinds of words, e.g., strong, fearsome, comforting, usually move you to change?

6. Who are messengers you know who remind you that God's kingdom is now?

Quotable Quotes

"Among those born of women no one is greater than John;
yet the least in the kingdom of God is greater than he." Luke 7:28

"The Lord called me before I was born,
while I was in my mother's womb he named me." Isaiah 49:1

Did You Know?

The church's liturgical calendar only celebrates three births: that of Jesus, Mary, and John the Baptist. All other saints' feasts are celebrated on the day of their death, the date of their birth into eternal life. John the Baptist was an important herald and witness to Christ, the true light of the world.

The Church Says:

John the Baptist is an important and pivotal figure in the Gospel. He was the last Jewish prophet and made the Savior known when he came. Stories surrounding John's birth, from the announcement by the angel and the striking mute of his father, Zechariah, to his leaping in Elizabeth's womb upon Mary's visitation to Elizabeth, are wonderful and are found in Luke's gospel. The clear and amazing action of God in his coming alerts the community that something new has begun. Some scholars believe John may have lived an ascetic life with the Essene community at Qumran. When he began his public ministry, he wore camel's hair cloth and ate locusts and wild honey. Coming out of the wilderness John preached a strong message of repentance to prepare the way for the savior's coming. Because he told Herod's brother it was unlawful to have a certain wife, Herod had him imprisoned and eventually had him beheaded to fulfill a request from Herodias daughter. In his preaching John continually prepared the way for Christ.

For This Feast:

I want to remember:

I want to put my faith into action by:

Questions to Explore

Prayer for this Feast

God, thank you for the gift of John the Baptist. When I hear your message to repent and change, may I listen and respond. Use me as your messenger to prepare the way for your fuller coming in our world today. Make my voice strong. Guide me in your truth. I pray through Christ, the light of the world. Amen.

Peter and Paul, Apostles

Scripture:

Acts 12:1-11
Psalm 34:2-3, 4-5, 6-7, 8-9
2 Timothy 4:6-8, 17-18
Matthew 16:13-19

Focus:

PAPACY AND COLLEGIALITY

Reflection

1. *What do you think it was like for Peter to be called rock by Christ, to have the keys be entrusted to him, and to live this out in his life?*

2. *What is an image of faith for you?*

3. *Name all the popes you are able to and anything you know about them.*

4. *State anything you know about Vatican Council II, e.g., when and where it was held, who attended, and any documents or results of the Council.*

5. *What are you aware of as being the work of the bishops conference in this country*

Quotable Quotes

"I have fought the good fight, I have finished the race, I have kept the faith." 2 Timothy 4:6-8

"Who do people say that the Son of Man is?" Matthew 16:13

"You are Peter, and on this rock I will build my church, and the gates of Hades will not prevail against it. I will give you the keys of the kingdom of heaven, and whatever you bind on earth will be bound in heaven, and whatever you loose on earth will be loosed in heaven." Matthew 16:18-19

Memorable People

Pope John XXIII convened Vatican Council II.

Pope John Paul II, who considers himself a missionary pope, has visited many countries and is known for kissing the ground of the country when he embarks from the airplane.

Did You Know?

Paul, who first persecuted the church, had his name changed by God from Saul at the time of his conversion. He is considered the preeminent missionary of the Gospel to the Gentile world.

Rocks have long denoted holy or special places. The various stones in the British Isles, e.g., Stonehenge, circles of stones in Avebury, stones in the form of a large Celtic cross in Callenish, Scotland and stones at Newgrange in Ireland, mark sacred sites.

The Church Says:

Simon, who was called rock (Peter) by Christ was given authority to bind and loose in the church on earth. With this authority Peter is considered the first Pope. All Popes succeed from Peter and share his authority. All of the bishops throughout the world are called the college of bishops, and together share authority for the church with the pope, who is the Bishop of Rome. The college of bishops may act only in accord with the papacy. The Second Vatican Council upheld the importance of the college of bishops.

For This Feast:

I want to remember:

I want to put my faith into action by:

Questions to Explore

Prayer for this Feast

God, I thank you for Peter and Paul
and their untiring and unwavering faith.
You have built the church upon
the rock of Peter's faith.
Bless the church with a solid faith.
May Paul's example inspire me and the entire
church to proclaim her faith.
May Peter and Paul's untiring witness
and prayers lead me to full life with Christ.
I pray through Christ, who is Lord
now and forever. Amen.

Scripture:

Daniel 7:9-10, 13-14
Psalm 97:1-2, 5-6, 9
2 Peter 1:16-19
Luke 9:28b-36

> **VISIONS AND PRIVATE REVELATIONS ARE MEANT TO ENCOURAGE THE BEHOLDER AND PROCLAIM THE GLORY OF GOD.**

Reflection

Meditation: Reflect on the experience of Hildegard of Bingen. She received visions that were interpreted with help from a voice from heaven. Here is a description of one vision: *"It happened that, in the eleven hundred and forty-first year of the Incarnation of the Son of God, Jesus Christ, when I was forty-two years and seven months old, Heaven was opened and a fiery light of exceeding brilliance came and permeated my whole breast, not like a burning but like a warming flame, as the sun warms anything its rays touch. And immediately I knew the meaning of the exposition of the Scriptures . . . I had sensed in myself wonderfully the power and mystery of secret and admirable visions from my childhood—that is, from the age of five—up to that time, as I do now. This, however, I showed to no one except a few religious persons who were living in the same manner as I."* [*Hildegard of Bingen, Scivias*, tr. by Mother Columba Hart and Jane Bishop (Mahwah, NJ: Paulist Press, 1990), p. 59-60.]

1. *Begin to write your experience and the feelings gleaned through this meditation.*

2. *Describe a time when you have had a similar experience of awe and wonder at God's glorified presence.*

Quotable Quotes

Perhaps St. John of the Cross speaks for all of the mystics down through the ages when he writes, "In giving his son, his only Word (for he possesses no other), he spoke everything to us in this sole Word— and he has no more to say . . . because what he spoke before to the prophets in parts, he has now spoken all at once by giving us the All Who is His Son. Any person questioning God or desiring some vision or revelation would be guilty not only of foolish behavior but also of offending him, by not fixing [their] eyes entirely upon Christ and by living with the desire for some other novelty."
(*The Ascent of Mount Carmel*, 2,22,3-5, in *The Collected Works*, trs. K. Kavanaugh, OCD, and O. Rodriguez, OCD, Institute of Carmelite Studies, Washington, D.C., 1979, p. 179-80, or LH, Second Week of Advent, Office of Readings)

Did You Know?

St. Bridget of Sweden, born into a noble family, married and had eight children, one of whom was St. Catherine of Sweden. With her husband she made a pilgrimage to St. James at Compostela, Spain, and at his death she entered religious life, eventually establishing a monastery for both nuns and monks. Making further pilgrimages to the Holy Land, she claimed to have visions of the nativity and the passion from the Virgin herself. These visions were recorded and became the basis for paintings, especially of the nativity. Mary is dressed in white, kneeling on the ground, with her cloak and shoes beside her and the naked child Jesus from which a brilliant light shines forth overpowering the candle held by Joseph. Grunewald's Isenheim altarpiece panel of the *Virgin and Child* is also associated with her visions. (*Oxford Companion to Christian Art and Architecture*, p. 66).

The Church Says:

In the history of Christian mysticism there are many examples of individual mystics who have claimed a private experience that communicates or reveals the activity of God. This extraordinary phenomenon may be comprised of images, ideas, or words. This communication of God to the mystic may result in physical, psychological or intellectual manifestations. The Marian apparitions at Lourdes and Fatima fall into this category of private revelation. Approved by the Church as credible, these apparitions are nonetheless not held by the Church to be part of the content of doctrine or teaching. The approval is stated in the negative, that there is nothing there which would harm the faith. As for the recent Marian apparitions at Medujorge, the Church has not yet conclude its investigation, although many pilgrims have visited this site and found solace and encouragement to their faith.

For This Feast:

I want to remember:

I want to put my faith into action by:

Questions to Explore

Prayer for this Feast

Jesus, you call us to follow you up
the high mountain to behold your glory.
We are dazzled by your transfigured presence
shining forth in
the face of a newborn baby,
the magnificence of the sunrise and sunset,
the sheer power of the wind.
Your revelation of the face of God
in all of creation
in our times of deep prayer
in the intimacy of friends and lovers;
Reassures us that you will come again in glory.
You come again, day after day
until that time when we will
behold you face-to-face. Amen.

The Assumption of the Virgin Mary into Heaven

Scripture:

Revelation 11:19a,12:1-6a, 10ab
Psalm 45:10-12,16
1 Corinthians 15:20-27
Luke 1:39-56

Focus:

MARY'S ASSUMPTION IS A SIGN OF HOPE FOR THE CHURCH.

Reflection

1. What does Mary's visit to Elizabeth and the Magnificat say about what kind of woman Mary was.

2. Name an image of Mary you want to carry with you.

3. What is your understanding of who Mary is for the church?

4. How do you view prayer to Mary?

5. How is this feast of Mary's assumption a sign of hope to the church?

Quotable Quotes

"A great portent appeared in heaven: a woman clothed with the sun, with the moon under her feet, and on her head a crown of twelve stars." Revelation 12:1

"Blessed are you among women, and blessed is the fruit of your womb." Luke 1:42

"My soul magnifies the Lord, and my spirit rejoices in God my Savior." Luke 1:46

Did You Know?

On November 1, 1950 Pope Pius XII made the Assumption of Mary an official dogma of the church in *Munificentissimus Deus*.

Mary is thought to have lived her last days with John the disciple in Ephesus.

Mary's death or her dormition, falling asleep, is portrayed on icons.

Zermatt, Switzerland, tucked in the shadow of the Matterhorn, annually holds a gigantic festival parade on the Feast of the Assumption.

The Church Says:

Mary, who was always a virgin and the mother of God, was assumed body and soul into heaven at the time of her death. This is an honor God bestowed upon Mary, the mother of Christ. This honor ranks Mary as higher than all the saints. As another human and as given to us as a mother at the foot of the cross, Mary's assumption is a sign of hope for the pilgrim church on earth. One day the church living and dead will be united at God's throne in heaven.

For This Feast:

I want to remember:

I want to put my faith into action by:

Questions to Explore

Prayer for this Feast

God of life and death, I praise you. Everything that has life comes from you. I praise you for Mary, who bore Christ in her womb, and whom you have raised body and soul to be with him in heaven. May I follow her example by responding wholeheartedly to you in all I say and do, and join with her someday in endless life and praise. I ask this through the risen Christ. Amen.

The Exaltation of the Holy Cross

Scripture:

Numbers 21:4b-9
Psalm 78:1-2, 34-35, 36-37, 38
Philippians 2:6-11
John 3:13-17

> **CHRIST SAVED US THROUGH THE CROSS, A SIGN OF VICTORY.**

Reflection

1. *How have you been lifted up and found life through the cross?*

2. *Given the context of Jesus being lifted up as the serpent in the desert, what does it mean to believe in Jesus?*

3. *What cross are you embracing now in your life that you believe will lead to fuller life in Christ?*

4. *What are some of the ways Christ is Savior?*

5. *What other titles, besides Savior, does the Church give to Jesus?*

Quotable Quotes

"He (Jesus) humbled himself and became obedient to the point of death—even death on a cross. Therefore God also highly exalted him." Philippians 2:8-9

". . . the cross, though it has at its heart a collision and contradiction, can extend its four arms forever without altering its shape. Because it has a paradox at its centre it can grow without changing. The circle returns upon itself and is bound. the cross opens its arms to the four winds; it is a signpost for free travelers." G. K. Chesterton

Did You Know?

Various forms of the cross are in use in the church. There is the form we are used to seeing upon which Jesus was hung, St. Brigid's cross with both sections being of equal length, the Tau Franciscan cross shaped like the Greek letter tau, the Celtic cross with a circle that cuts across the four sections of the cross, and the Jerusalem cross, which in addition to the four cross- sections has smaller crosses in each of the four quadrants.

Many churches and baptismal fonts are constructed in the shape of a cross.

The expression "tree of life" comes from contrasting the cross to the tree in the garden of Eden. The tree in Eden, the means of the first human sin through which death came into the world, is the tree of death. The cross is the tree of life.

The Church Says:

The cross has become for Christians a sign of hope and of victory. Through death on the cross, Jesus was raised to new life. The mystery is that through embracing the cross with Christ we are brought to new life. That is at the heart of the Christian faith. Sin and evil symbolized in death do not have ultimate power. God's love is more powerful. God reigns over everything. Christianity involves facing and embracing the cross that presents itself in various forms in life. Through his death on the cross, Jesus atones for our sins, or reconciles all things to himself. Christ is the Savior who saves through liberating, bringing good news, giving sight, freeing the oppressed, forgiving and healing. Christ lifts us up and is our sign of healing.

For This Feast:

I want to remember:

I want to put my faith into action by:

Questions to Explore

Prayer for this Feast

Loving and gracious God, through Christ you teach me that the cross is not only a means of suffering, but also a cross of triumph. I place the crosses I bear in your hands. Through bearing my cross with Christ, may I one day share in his glorious resurrection. I pray, through Christ, my Savior. Amen.

Scripture:

Revelation 7:2-4, 9-14
Psalm 24:1-2, 3-4, 5-6
1 John 3:1-3
Matthew 5:1-12a

Focus:

COMMUNION OF SAINTS

Reflection

Directions: *Rewrite the Beatitudes, by translating them for your life. It may be helpful to note that the first four are attitudes or postures that describe the simplicity of the 'little ones' before God and the last four describe actions for building God's kingdom of justice.*

Blessed are the poor in spirit, for theirs is the
kingdom of heaven.
Blessed are
For

Blessed are they who mourn, for they will be
comforted.
Blessed are
For

Blessed are the meek, for they will inherit the land.
Blessed are
For

Blessed are they who hunger and thirst for
righteousness, for they will be satisfied.
Blessed are
For

Blessed are the clean of heart, for they will see God.
Blessed are
For

Blessed are the peacemakers, for they will be called
children of God.
Blessed are
For

Blessed are they who are persecuted for the sake of
righteousness, for theirs is the kingdom of heaven.
Blessed
For

Questions

1. *What attitudes and actions are you challenged to acquire in your daily journey of conversion?*

2. *What makes this 'impossible' challenge a lived reality for all God's people?*

Quotable Quotes

"There is an element in the veneration of saints of which Catholics themselves are often unconscious. The cult of the saints excludes the cult of success—the veneration of people who have got on well in this world, the snobbish admiration of wealth and fame. This does not mean that a person who apparently has succeeded in the world and has led a happy life is necessarily a bad Christian who must be prepared for a painful settlement with his God and Judge when he comes to die. But it does mean that the religious business instinct which has caused people to imagine that the material welfare of individuals or nations is a sign of God's special favor, or to see in disasters and defeats a punishment form God—that is opposed by the Church in her veneration of saints. . . .Whenever she celebrates Mass in red vestments it is a protest against this." (Sigrid Undset, *Stages on the Road*, tr. By Arthur G. Chater (NY: Alfred A. Knopf, 1934) p. VI-VII.)

Did You Know?

The remote origins of this feast are found in the honor that early Christians paid to the martyrs, remembering them on the anniversary of their death, very often at the very place of their martyrdom. After the age of persecution had ended, other holy individuals were gradually added to the list of those commemorated annually. In the fourth century, saints were named in the Eucharistic Prayer. By the fifth century, a feast of All Saints was celebrated in certain churches of the Christian East. When Pope Boniface transformed the Roman pantheon into a Christian church on May 13, 610, he designated that day as a feast of all saints. It was under Gregory IV that the feast was moved to November 1, and thenceforth the observance spread throughout the West.

The Church Says:

One of the credal affirmations is belief in the "communion of saints." What is meant by this phrase? The Catechism asserts quite simply and clearly that the communion of saints is the Church. The Church forms one body, with Christ as its head, who shares his riches with all the members through the sacraments. Those riches, governed by one and the same Spirit throughout all the members, are considered as one common fund. The term, therefore, indicates both a sharing in holy things (the riches of Christ) and a sharing among a holy people (we who are claimed for God in Christ).

Thus, in the New Testament, "the saints" refers to the whole body of believers, the Church. But, in terms of the formal, papal procedure for the recognition of saints, the term refers to those men and women who throughout our Christian history who have been outstanding in holiness, sometimes heroic in their efforts to witness to the kingdom of God.

For This Feast:

I want to remember:

I want to put my faith into action by:

Questions to Explore

Prayer for this Feast

Holy God, we praise you
for setting before us
the witness of so many
who have gone before us in faith.
All the martyrs,
virgins,
widows,
teacher,
holy men and women
known for their actions on behalf of your kingdom.
We join with them as they cry out,
"Salvation comes from our God,
who is seated on the throne,
and from the Lamb." (Rev. 7:19)
"Amen, Blessing and glory,
wisdom and thanksgiving, honor,
power and might be to our God
forever and ever. Amen." (Rev. 7:12)

Scripture:

Readings for All Souls may be taken from any of the Masses for the Dead. See the Lectionary nn. 789-93.

Focus:

PURGATORY

Reflection

Directions: *In the space below write your own obituary, as you would like it to read at your death. Use the following as reference questions: When were you born? When did you die? What was the cause of your death? Who survived you? What will you be most remembered for? What was your biggest regret?*

Quotable Quotes

"Life is not lost by dying;
life is lost minute by minute, day by day,
in all the small uncaring ways."

Steven Vincent Benet

Did You Know?

In Dante's *Divine Comedy*, Purgatory is a mountain rising from the ocean and divided into terraces, at the top of which is terrestrial paradise. Thomas Merton used Dante's image of a seven tiered mountain as the symbol of the modern world in his autobiography *The Seven Storey Mountain*.

The Church Says:

In our Catholic understanding, purgatory is a state of purification between death and heaven whereby the remaining obstacles to the full enjoyment of one's personal and eternal union with God are removed. The obstacles which are removed are venial sins not repented at the time of death and any remaining effects or consequences to one's person of repented and forgiven mortal or deadly sins committed during one's earthly life. In our Catholic understanding, purgatory is not an opportunity to reverse the course of one's earthly life. Conversion is not possible in purgatory if conversion did not take place in life before death. Since an individual judgment follows immediately upon death, purgatory is that interval after death that erases conditions preventing persons from enjoying full fellowship with God.

It is important to note that while Scripture refers to a cleansing fire (1 Cor 3:15; 1 Pt 1:7) and burning flames figure in some artistic depictions of purgatory, the operative notion in Catholic doctrine and theology on purgatory is that it is a state of purification not punishment (CCC 1031). This state may even last only an instant, as we count time. What the doctrine upholds is that purgatory is a transitional state which makes one ready for the experience of seeing God face to face in heaven.

It is also important to note that the doctrine of purgatory upholds an unbroken liturgical practice in our Church to making intercessory prayers for the dead. The Second Vatican Council observes, "In full consciousness of this communion of the whole Mystical Body of Jesus Christ, the Church in its pilgrim members, from the very earliest days of the Christian religion, has honored with great respect the memory of the dead; and, 'because it is a holy and a wholesome thought to pray for the dead that they may be loosed from their sins' (2 Mac 12:46) she offers her suffrages for them." (LG, 50).

For This Feast:

I want to remember:

I want to put my faith into action by:

Questions to Explore

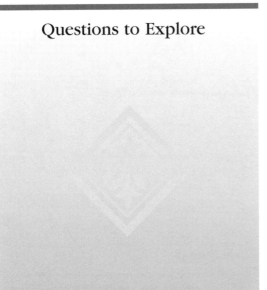

Prayer for this Feast

Prayer for the Souls in Purgatory:

*Eternal rest grant unto them, O Lord,
and may perpetual light shine upon them.
Amen.*

Dedication of St. John Lateran

Scripture:

Ezekiel 47:1-2, 8-9, 12
Psalm 84:3-6, 8, 11
1 Corinthians 3:9c-11, 16-17
John 2:13-22

Focus:

THE FOUR MARKS OF THE CHURCH

Reflection

Directions: *Reflect on and write your responses to the following questions: How do you feel about becoming a member of a universal church? What hesitations, concerns, or questions do you have?*

Questions

1. *What gift does being a part of a universal church offer to you?*

2. *How are you called as an individual and as a community to work for unity among churches?*

3. *How do you hear yourself being called to holiness?*

Did You Know?

The Lateran basilica is filled with venerable relics. The high altar itself is constructed over a wooden table which, as legend has it, St. Peter celebrated the Eucharist with the ancient Christians of Rome.
(Mary Ellen Hynes, *Companion to the Calendar*, LTP, Archdiocese of Chicago, 1993, p 166)

The famous Lateran Treaty or "Concordat" agreed upon between the Vatican and Mussolini was finalized and signed at the Lateran Palace. The agreement stipulates that the Lateran grounds are also considered part of Vatican City State.

The Church Says:

The feast we celebrate today observes the anniversary of the dedication of the cathedral church of Rome. When the Emperor Constantine officially recognized Christianity, he made generous gifts to the Church, one of which was a palace and grounds formerly belonging to the Laterani family. In 324 he added a large church on the grounds named the Basilica of the Savior. Legend has it that the basilica was dedicated on November 9 that year. Later a baptistry was added and dedicated to St. John the Baptist. In subsequent years the entire edifice became known as St. John of the Lateran. Because it is the cathedral church of the bishop of Rome, the feast, at first observed only in Rome, was later extended to the whole Church as a sign of devotion to and of unity with the Chair of Peter. Thus, while this feast originates in a particular edifice in a particular place, it truly celebrates the universal Church which is apostolic, catholic, holy and one.

For This Feast:

I want to remember:

I want to put my faith into action by:

Questions to Explore

Prayer for this Feast

Nicene Creed

We believe in one God,
the Father, the Almighty,
maker of heaven and earth,
of all that is seen and unseen.

We believe in one Lord, Jesus Christ,
the only son of God,
eternally begotten of the Father,
God from God, Light from Light,
true God from true God,
begotten, not made, one in being with
the Father.
Through him all things were made.
For us men ad for our salvation
he came down from heaven:

by the power of the Holy Spirit
he was born of the Virgin Mary, and
became man.

For sake he was crucified under
Pontius Pilate;

he suffered, died, and was buried.
On the third day he rose again
in fulfillment of the Scriptures;
he ascended into heaven
and is seated at the right hand of
the Father.
He will come again in glory to judge the
living and the dead,
and his kingdom will have no end.

We believe in the Holy Spirit, the Lord, the
giver of life,
who proceeds from the Father and the Son.
With the Father and the Son he is wor-
shipped and glorified.
He has spoken through the Prophets.
We believe in one holy catholic and apos-
tolic church.
We acknowledge one baptism for the for-
giveness of sins.
We look for the resurrection of the dead,
and the life of the world to come. Amen.

Glossary of Terms

Note: Those terms which display an asterisk* are themselves described elsewhere in the glossary.

Almsgiving

is the religious practice of giving from one's financial resources in order to assist or help those who are poorer and in need. This is commended by Jesus (Luke 18:22). St. Paul exhorts members of the Christian community at Corinth to give alms that they might be enriched by their very generous giving (2 Corinthinans 9:11). On Ash Wednesday we Catholics hear from Matthew's gospel—where Jesus teaches us to fast, pray, and give alms (Matthew 6:1-6,16-18). Almsgiving is considered one of the three central penitential activities of Lent and a work of mercy. (The seven corporal works of mercy are: to feed the hungry, to give drink to the thirsty, to clothe the naked, to visit prisoners, to give shelter to the homeless, to visit the sick and to bury the dead). The word "alms" derives from the Greek, *eleos*, or "pity."

Anointing

is the coating, covering or touching of a person or object with oil to convey a religious significance. The Old Testament refers to Moses' action in anointing the meeting tent, the ark of the covenant and related religious objects with a special mixture of oil indicating the sacred status of these objects. Aaron and his sons were also anointed as priests (Exodus 30:27-30). Prophets and kings of Israel were anointed. The word "Christ" comes from the term "anointed" and is the title bestowed upon Jesus in the New Testament letters of Paul indicating his role as priestly, prophetic and kingly Messiah, the Lord's Anointed One who saves us (Isaiah 61:1). In contemporary liturgical usage, the Oil of Catechumens is used to anoint prior to baptism and has its roots in ancient times when athletes were anointed before wrestling competitions. Sacred Chrism, a mixture of oil and perfume consecrated by the bishop, is used to anoint after Baptism, at Confirmation and at the Ordination of priests and bishops. The Oil of the Sick is used to anoint sick persons and is specifically referenced in the New Testament (James 5). Chrism is also used to anoint altars and churches when they are dedicated.

Blessing

is the ritual expression of God's goodness and love. The action has traditionally communicated either the blessings of divine gifts bestowed upon us or our thankfulness for those gifts. Blessings are liturgical signs which call down God's holiness upon people or things. *The Book of Blessings* is a ritual book of the Church which lists several hundred prayer texts that express various types of blessings for individuals, groups and objects. Types range from blessings of pregnant mothers, to catechists, to stained glass windows. The act of blessing is usually accomplished through certain prayers spoken and raising hands in benediction over the person or object, including making the Sign of the Cross.

Candidate

in the Catechumenate refers to a person who is baptized in another faith and who will be completing Christian initiation by being formally received into the Catholic Church. This term is also used in referring to a baptized Catholic who is seeking to complete Christian initiation through the celebration of Confirmation and Eucharist. Anyone seeking a sacrament may be referred to as a candidate.

Canonization

is the process undertaken by the Church which leads to the declaration of sainthood. In the early Church the martyrs (those who died for the faith) were honored on the anniversary of their death and confessors (those who suffered for the faith) were also venerated. Later, exemplary Christians who led heroic lives of holiness were also acclaimed as saints. Beginning in the thirteenth century, the process became more formal. Recently, Pope John Paul II issued an apostolic constitution, *Divinus Perfectionis Magister* (Divine Teacher and Model of Perfection) in 1983 which simplified the canonization process. Initially, a local bishop oversees the investigation into the life of the person in question, after which, a biography, published writings and information regarding possible miracles are submitted to the Vatican. The first step on the road to canonization is beatification (honoring the person with the title of "blessed"). If all requirements are met, then the person is canonized (given the title of "saint," which derives from the Latin for "holy") by a declaration of the Pope at a solemn liturgy*.

Catechism

(from the Greek, *katechein*, "to echo," or "to resound down"), a manual of religious instruction usually presented in a simple and clear format. One of the first Catholic manuals was published after the Council of Trent in 1566 and intended to assist the clergy. An early catechism used in the United States was the *Baltimore Catechism*, commissioned by the bishops in 1885. In 1992 the Vatican issued the *Catechism of the Catholic Church*, a compendium of teachings which relies on Scripture, Tradition* and the teaching office (magisterium) of the Church.

Catechumen

refers to a person who has attained the age of reason who is not baptized and who seeks Christian initiation (Baptism, Confirmation and Eucharist). One becomes a catechumen when the Church celebrates the Rite of Acceptance into the Order of Catechumens. This rite* is normally celebrated after the completion of a period of Inquiry or Pre-catechumenate, the first stage of the initiation process.

Contemplation

describes a particular prayer form which relies less on thinking and systematic thought processes and more on the direct experience of God's presence. While systematic meditation* may lead to contemplative prayer, this form is generally considered a gift from God and not the result of what one is doing in praying. Contemplation is described by many spiritual writers as the deepest type of prayer that involves the core of a person's being.

Conversion

characterizes the changes that occur in a person who embraces Jesus Christ. Those changes can be simultaneously evidenced in thought, word and deed. Conversion takes place gradually over a period of time.

Creed

from the Latin, *credo*, "I believe," a pithy, official formulation of the tenets of the faith. The Apostles' Creed and the Nicene Creed are the two best-known examples of Christian creeds (either is mandated for use at Sunday Mass when the Church confesses its faith liturgically). In the course of Christian history, there have come down to us other creeds, such as the Athanasian Creed and the Creed of Hippolytus.

Discernment

describes the attempt to sift through an individual's or a group's experience to determine the call of the divine and where the Holy Spirit may be leading. It has also been called "Christian decision-making." It should be understood that discernment is on-going in the life of the follower of Jesus and relies on private and liturgical prayer, the use of Scripture and sometimes also the assistance of a Spiritual Director.

Doctrine

from Latin, *doctrina*, or "teaching," is an official statement by the Church of some aspect of teaching. Doctrine taught infallibly is also called a dogma*. In the Roman Catholic Church doctrine is formulated by the bishops acting together in concert with the Pope, such as at a synod or an ecumenical council. Core teachings or doctrines are also contained in Scripture and thus the Word of God "measures" all subsequent doctrinal statements.

Dogma

from Greek for "what seems right," this term describes a definitive teaching of the Church given infallibly (without error). The ability to declare a doctrine* infallible rests with the Pope who does so in two areas: faith and morals.

Elect/Election

is the term applied to those catechumens who have been called by the Church to the celebration of the initiation sacraments (Baptism, Confirmation and Eucharist) at Easter. The local Bishop gives voice to this call at the celebration of the Rite of Election. In this sense, election does not describe the result of a political process or voting, but the action of God through the agency of the Church. In Sacred Scripture the elect are those freely chosen by God to receive the gift of salvation and to bear witness to God.

Exorcism

is the Church's prayer which seeks to free persons from the power of evil. The New Testament reports that Jesus and his disciples engaged in such liberating actions. In the history of the Church two forms of exorcism have evolved. Major (or solemn) exorcisms seek to free a person from a persistent spiritual condition. Today these forms of exorcism are restricted to bishops or those priests whom they specially delegate. The other type of exorcism is found in the process of Christian initiation and consist of prayers and gestures expressing the Church's desire that those to be baptized be delivered from temptation and the power of evil. These "Minor Exorcisms" may be celebrated during the stage of the catechumenate. The "Scrutinies," which contain exorcism prayers, are celebrated on the third, fourth and fifth Sundays of Lent with the elect*. The ritual used for the baptism of infants also contains a prayer of exorcism.

Fasting

is the activity whereby a person restricts the amount of food eaten to only one full meal per day. It can be in the context of a special time in that person's life, perhaps a retreat or an intense period of prayer. The Church requires all adult members in good health to fast on Good Friday as a penitential action and invites this fasting to continue into the day on Holy Saturday as a joyful preparation for the celebration of Easter.

Inquirer

describes a person in the first stage of the process of Christian initiation.

Lectionary

is the ritual book which contains the Scripture selections to be read at Mass, both weekday and Sunday celebrations, arranged in accordance with the liturgical seasons*. The Lectionary, as revised by the Second Vatican Council, offers three readings for Sundays along with a psalm text. The first reading is usually from the Old Testament, the second reading is taken from a non-gospel New Testament text, and the third reading is taken from one of the gospel accounts. A three-year cycle apportions out each of the synoptic Gospels over the course of the Sundays of that year. John's Gospel is read at Easter, on special feasts and fills in on the year given over to Mark.

Liturgical Season

refers to the various periods of time in the Church calendar which are annually celebrated. There are five such seasons: Advent, Christmas, Lent, Easter and Ordinary Time. Through the unfolding of this annual cycle of seasons, the Church celebrates the Paschal Mystery* of Jesus Christ. Thus, the very passage of time itself becomes a holy observance.

Liturgy

from Greek, *leitourgia*, "public works," this term denotes the communal, public and official worship of the Church contained in texts and rites* celebrated by the people of God when they gather. As the original Greek suggests, this activity is the work of the whole Church and does not lie with any one person or group. The entire household of the faithful does the liturgy and in so doing directs itself to the praise and glory of God.

Meditation

is a particular form of prayer whereby one purposely focuses attention. This focus may be achieved by concentrating on a singular image or object. Suitable objects for Christian meditation include texts of Sacred Scripture, religious artwork, events in the life of Christ, images of Mary and the saints and events of everyday life which heighten one's awareness of God.

Monasticism

derives from the Greek, *monos*, or "one, alone," describing the institutional pursuit of religious life where individuals take vows of poverty, chastity and obedience, separating themselves from the world either alone (as hermits) or in community. Monasticism attempts under the guidance of a rule (for example, the Rule of St. Benedict) to establish a life of prayer and work for the glory of God, for the personal holiness of the individual, and for the good of the Church and the world. Different monastic orders sometimes take their name from the founder of their rule, such as the Benedictines (St. Benedict), Franciscans (St. Francis of Assisi), and Dominicans (St. Dominic).

Neophyte

from Greek, *neophutos*, or "new plant, new growth," this term refers to those newly initiated who have celebrated Baptism, Confirmation and Eucharist. Neophytes, the newly initiated, are grafted onto Christ as vines to the branch and are so designated up until the first anniversary of their initiation.

Paschal Mystery

is the term encompassing Jesus' suffering, death, burial, resurrection, ascension and sending of the Holy Spirit. It refers to the saving activity of Jesus by which we are redeemed and given new life by the gracious love of God.

Purification and Enlightenment

is the third stage of Christian initiation. It begins on the First Sunday of Lent and concludes on Holy Saturday as the Easter Vigil commences.

Reflection

is similar to meditation but not as intense an activity. In reflection, one concentrates mental activity and takes the time and effort to carefully consider.

Rite

describes ceremonial activity that proceeds from specific liturgical rules or directions. Some examples are the Rite of Infant Baptism, the Rite of Christian Initiation of Adults, and the Rite of Anointing and Pastoral Care of the Sick. Not only these ritual books, but all of the rites currently in use by the Church were revised at the direction of the Second Vatican Council.

Rite of Christian Initiation of Adults (RCIA)

is the ritual book in which the Church describes the formation process of Christian initiation. The Second Vatican Council called for the restoration of the ancient process of initiation which included stages of growth and conversion in Christ marked by steps or liturgical celebrations. The four stages in initiation are: Inquiry, Catechumenate, Purification and Enlightenment and Mystagogy. The Rite of Acceptance into the Order of Catechumens is the step between Inquiry and the Catechumenate. The Rite of Election is the step which celebrates the beginning of Purification and Enlightenment. And celebrating initiation (Baptism, Confirmation and Eucharist) signals the step into Mystagogy.

Sacrament

from Latin, *sacramentum*, or "oath, pledge" which originally meant the oath taken by soldiers and office holders of the Roman Empire, but became the term used by the Church to indicate its seven foremost ritual celebrations. The seven sacraments are: Baptism, Confirmation, Eucharist, Marriage, Holy Orders, Reconciliation and Anointing of the Sick. In these seven sacraments, God's love is expressed and grace is communicated. The saving life, death and resurrection of Jesus (Paschal Mystery*) is the foundation and basis for the seven sacraments celebrated by the Church.

Sacramentals

are sacred signs instituted by the Church which while they do not bear the same impact as the seven sacraments, nonetheless dispose people to holiness and an openness to God's grace imparted and experienced in the seven sacraments. Examples of sacramentals include blessings, exorcisms, and the use of holy water, rosaries, and sacred images in prayer.

Scrutiny

is the name given to the ritual celebrations occurring on the Third, Fourth and Fifth Sundays of Lent during the stage of initiation known as Purification and Enlightenment*. Within the Scrutiny celebrations, a laying on of hands and an exorcism* prayer expresses the Church's concern for the elect*, as the community of the faithful prays that not only the elect but all God's children be delivered from the power of evil.

Sponsor

describes the ministry of spiritual companion to a catechumen as he or she moves through the various stages of the initiation process up to the celebration of the Rite of Election when the person is then accompanied by a "Godparent." A baptized candidate* is accompanied by a sponsor throughout the whole initiation process.

Tradition

describes the living reality by which all of the Church's beliefs expressed doctrinally, its sacred writings expressed in Scripture, and its prayer expressed in rituals are handed down and transmitted from one generation to the next under the guidance of the Holy Spirit. The Second Vatican Council articulated an understanding of Tradition as the whole life and activity of the Church which helps men and women to be holy in this world. It is the totality of God's revelation preserved and cherished by the household of the faithful.